NITHYA YOGA

Based on the teachings of
Paramahamsa Nithyananda

PUBLISHED BY NITHYANANDA VEDIC SCIENCES UNIVERSITY PRESS
A division of Nithyananda Vedic Sciences University, USA

CONTENTS

Gratitude

There is no one greater in the three worlds than the guru.
It is he who grants divine knowledge (divya-jnana)
and should therefore be worshipped with supreme devotion.

Yoga-Shikha-Upanishad (5.53)

To Dakshinamurthy, the Guru of all gurus, to Patanjali, the great scientist of the inner world and to Raghupati Yogi for initiating me into the Science of Yoga with such love and care. And, to all the Masters down the ages for dedicating their lives to preserve, update and impart the traditions of Yoga, I offer my respects and gratitude.

In the lineage of Patanjali

When a master transfers his energy to a disciple, it is in that moment that the spiritual lineage carries on....
It is perennial, this lineage of Patanjali.

Who was Patanjali?

There is complete uncertainty as to who Patanjali was. Some think of him as the divine incarnation of the serpent *Ananta,* who supports the whole universe and is simultaneously the bed of Lord Vishnu. Factually, next to nothing is known about him. It is believed that he was born in Southern India, in the holy town of Chidambaram, a place very deeply associated with the dancing expression of Lord Shiva, as *Nataraja.* Hindu tradition identifies him with a famous grammarian of the same name who lived in the second century B.C.E.

The reason for this confusion is that India has known of several other Patanjali's. The name Patanjali is said to be given to *Ananta* because he wanted to teach yoga on earth and fell *(pat)* from heaven, onto the palm *(anjali)* of Gonika, his mother.

Notwithstanding his origin, Patanjali is credited with the compilation of the great book, the *Yoga Sutra.* It is an exceptionally open and profound work on the nature of consciousness. It is considered more universal than any other book because it focuses only on the mind, its qualities, influences and fluctuations and the resultant disturbances that are obstacles on the path of the discovery of the Self. It clearly outlines the means to transcend the mind and live in the heightened state of awareness called *samadhi.* Because the mind is common to all of human kind, these *sutra,* therefore, are of interest to all.

A *sutra* is a style of writing, which has very few words, is yet full of essence, is affirmative, universal in context and yet free from all ambiguity. These *sutra,* these aphorisms on yoga are scientific, straightforward and to the core. This is the greatest book ever presented to mankind. Millions of books and many styles of yoga have stemmed from this one book. The *Yoga Sutra* is so complete that not one single word more can be added to it.

Though Patanjali had his roots deeply in the Vedic tradition, he did not propogate any *isms* (religions). Patanjali was a saint and a scientist rolled into one. He declared universal truth for the

Patanjali - the Father of Yoga

benefit of all mankind. He left behind a strong energy, a strong understanding and a strong way for people to experience universal consciousness. Patanjali has either directly or indirectly influenced every spiritual teacher on planet earth.

One such great teacher was Raghupati yogi, from the small temple town of Tiruvannamalai, in Southern India.

Arrival of Raghupati yogi

When Paramahamsa Nithyananda was about three years old, a relative brought home a wandering mendicant, or *sanyasi* whose name was Raghupati yogi. Raghupati yogi lived on the same street as Paramahamsa and came to know the entire family. He was born and brought up in Burma (Myanmar) then a British Colony, where he had learnt yogic procedures from Buddhist lamas. He was an adept in yoga and related methods and could demonstrate many yogic powers, including the ability to levitate at will which he mastered through a combination of yogic postures *(asana)* and breath control techniques *(pranayama)*. Paramahamsa fondly remembers the numerous occasions when Raghupati yogi would levitate and playfully ask the children to

Raghupati Yogi

crawl under him; it was an entertaining game that everyone enjoyed thoroughly!

Raghupathi yogi was an expert in Patanjali's *Ashtanga Yoga* methods and taught it diligently to his most ardent student, Paramahamsa.

Raghupati yogi noticed that the young Paramahamsa, unlike boys of his age who played with toys and marbles, was engrossed in playing with little idols and statues of gods and goddesses. They seemed to be his companions and he was very comfortable playing with them. Being a man of such deep wisdom, Raghupati yogi realized that Paramahamsa was a highly evolved spiritual soul. He remarked that the boy was a light that had started shining in that household. Despite the huge age difference between them, Paramahamsa was totally at ease in the company of Raghupati yogi. They seemed to share a deep bond where the need for communication did not matter.

Paramahamsa remembers Raghupati yogi with tremendous affection and respect. He recalls...

'I had the fortune to study yoga under a great master of yoga, Raghupati yogi. He was also conferred the title Yogiraj and was known as Yogiraj Yogananda Puri. When I spent time around him he was aged around one hundred and four or five. He was a very healthy man who had mastered yoga and who had experienced all aspects of yoga; not just in the physical level, however in much deeper ways. He would express many different powers of yoga.

I remember very clearly he would take a stone and make the sound of a hammer hitting the stone; the stone would break into two pieces. Sometimes he would make the sound of a stone flying and to my astonishment I would see birds falling down as if they had been the targets! At other times he would create a particular vibration and snakes would come from the bushes!

IN THE LINEAGE OF PATANJALI

Similarly he would create the sound of a dog and from all over dogs would gather around him. Just through sound he was able to do anything he wanted to do.

He had amazing strength and unimaginable physical power, which he expressed so casually. He would tie an iron rope around his chest and exhale completely, then he would inhale deeply and the rope would break into pieces!

Usually a logical mind cannot accept or understand that all this is possible, but this great yogi made everything possible! I had the fortune to be around him and see him levitating, not once but at least twenty times. He would inhale deeply and hold the breath. The moment he did that the body would lift from the ground, like an inflated balloon!

From the age of three to thirteen I had the fortune to be under his feet, his guidance and care. Every day from morning till noon for at least 4 to 5 hours, he would make me do all of the traditional yogic techniques including asana (postures). He would instruct me to bend this way and that way, backwards and forwards. He would make me do all of the yogic cleansing techniques like neti, dhauti. I would have to swallow that long cloth to clean the intestine and the internal system.

To tell you honestly, it's only now that I feel happy about everything he used to make me do. Those days I used to hate him because from morning around 6 am he would start my training. It was practically like torture; any beginner in yoga can sympathize and understand what I am talking about.'

Raghupati yogi came into Paramahamsa's life for a purpose. Being a yogi of many great skills and powers, he helped prepare Paramahamsa's body to receive and hold the tremendous energy of enlightenment. Paramahamsa says retaining this tremendous energy is like squeezing four elephants into a small hut.

Paramahamsa says experiencing a *satori* (a glimpse of enlightenment or a no-mind state) is not a big thing; anybody can experience a *satori*. However, for somebody to stay in that level of consciousness and to actually express it, preparation of the body and mind is required. Raghupati yogi helped prepare Paramahamsa's body and mind through various yogic techniques. He enabled him to experience, remain and radiate the high energy of enlightenment.

Raghupati yogi would without fail come to Paramahamsa's house every morning. The yogi would take him to the temple and for three to four hours make him practice yoga techniques. Day after day, he would make the boy do these yogic exercises.

Paramahamsa age 10

Paramahamsa recalls affectionately:

'The temple where Raghupahti yogi used to teach me yogic techniques had a beautiful stone pillared mandapam (hall). He would instruct me to climb all of the stone pillars; 20 to 30 pillars continuously! When climbing the pillars, he told me I was not allowed to use both hands to climb. I could use only one! The other hand was to be kept behind my back or tied with a rope. To this day, I am still not able to find any reference to support why he made me climb the pillars. I have not read any Yogic literature which identifies that climbing pillars is a yogic technique!'

Pillars in the krithika mandapam where Paramahamsa received yogic training under Raghupati Yogi

The boy obeyed Raghupati yogi, partly out of respect and partly out of affection. The yogi insisted that Paramahamsa do this extended practice every day. He told the boy that he needed to keep his body fit, as he would need to do Herculean things in the future. After the yoga practice, he would take Paramahamsa to a nearby hotel to have breakfast. He was very loving and brought him candies and chocolates to keep the boy's interest alive.

Over time, Raghupati yogi taught all eight parts of *Ashtanga Yoga,* including *pranayama* (breath control techniques) and *asana* (postures) to Paramahamsa. Additionally, he taught *mantra, dhyana* (meditation) and various other yogic techniques. Paramahamsa was also given the invaluable knowledge of how to live without water and not feel thirsty, by twisting the tongue, sucking in air while sounding the mantra '*lam*'. He also taught Paramahamsa how to go without sleep, without feeling tired and

how to live without food and not feel hunger, by using a herb to draw a diagram on the skin over the liver.

Paramahamsa was also taught how to play with light energy and how to create things through sound energy. These were of immense use to him during his wandering days and penance; but for these techniques and the strength built through yoga, his body-mind would have been unable to withstand the rigors of those years of tough ascetic life.

Raghupati yogi did a great service by preparing Paramahamsa's body and mind for his future endeavors. He also had fulfillment. As much as Paramahamsa learnt from him, the yogi said he learnt from the boy. He gave Paramahamsa the deerskin he used to sit on, which was given to him by his Master. This was treated and tanned with herbs and even after 60 odd years it has the original hair still intact.

Raghupati yogi arranged for taking pictures of Paramahamsa in various meditative postures during his years with him. Photography was very expensive those days in rural India. Raghupati yogi had borrowed money from a local hotel owner, Upadhyaya, for these photographs. When asked why he was doing it at such expense, he just smiled and never answered. When the photos were delivered, he wrote on them, 'The whole world will one day thank me for these photographs.' Raghupati yogi had photos taken of Paramahamsa alone as well as the two of them together, but none of himself alone. When questioned about this by Paramahamsa, Raghupati yogi just smiled and said, 'No one will want to have my photographs, but many will have yours!'

Importance of early training

Raghupati yogi told Paramahamsa that the age to learn yoga is before 14 and that's why he started him at 3 years of age. He had in total a full ten years to train the young boy.

Paramahamsa says that the rigorous training he underwent in the first eleven years of his life helped in sustaining the tremendous energy of enlightenment. He remembers very clearly Raghupati yogi telling him that to bear fruit on the spiritual path you have to be trained from a very young age.

According to Vedic traditions any kind of spiritual practice must be undertaken before sexual maturity. If it is done so, it is easy to live with reality and not fall prey to impossible and unreal fantasies. Otherwise, the whole process can be difficult and disheartening. The reason is, once puberty is attained, the fantasies and imagination that are thrust on the individual through the outside world, (in the modern context the media, peer pressure and social conditioning), play havoc with the hormones and the vital energies. It then becomes very difficult to begin the practice of yoga for spiritual elevation. At best it can be viewed as the practice for granting physical and mental well-being.

Sitting with the Guru, true learning happens
The Vedic Renaissance -
Brahmachari's of the Nithyananda Order

During the Vedic times the practice of *brahmacharya* was all about learning to live with reality. *Brahma* means 'truth, reality' and *charya* means 'to walk with'. This understanding has more to do with learning about and accepting reality. In no way did it mean forced celibacy, as many people have erroneously understood it.

This truth was very well known during the Vedic times. That is why in ancient India the *gurukulam (*the educational system) was highly regarded. When a child was about 3 years old, the parents handed the child over to the guru, who from then on became its father and mother.

Till the age of seven, children were allowed to roam freely, unclothed or wearing a single loose robe with no awareness of their gender. The energies were allowed to flow easily. Restrictions were not imposed on the children in this extremely natural atmosphere. Both boys and girls were taught the *Gayatri mantra* (sacred chant) so that the inner sun, their innate intelligence, would be awakened and expressed.

With such unique and caring guidance, most children would have some kind of spiritual experience by puberty. As the Guru had trained their body and mind so lovingly, they were capable of handling the subtle high voltage energies that coursed through their bodies.

Raghupati yogi's appearance in Paramahamsa's childhood was indeed most propitious. He was very learned and would pass on as many teachings as possible to the young lad. It was as if he wanted to pour all his experience and knowledge in the little time that was available to him.

Paramahamsa remembers that at all times Raghupati yogi would play with snakes, which for him, was initially quite frightening. He would playfully guide thin snakes through his nostrils and take them out through his mouth in imitation of some yogic cleansing techniques. When Raghupati yogi saw the boy's fear, he would laugh and say that they would not do any harm, as they were a part of him, his family. He always wore a gold girdle around his waist like a coiled snake around a pillar.

It was only after enlightenment that Paramahamsa understood that he had received his training and initiation in the Science of Yoga and other spiritual matter from a yogi who had experienced the consciousness of Patanjali.

Paramahamsa meditating at the foot of Arunachala in his young age.
He can be seen here seated on the deer skin given to him by Raghupati Yogi.

Yoga

'*Before knowing what yoga is, it is important to know what yoga is not. Yoga is neither a physical exercise nor is it breath control. These are but a part of yoga.*'

- *Paramahamsa*

Go Deep…

Someone once asked Paramahamsa 'What is your impression of yoga and how it is being practiced in the West?' Paramahamsa answered,

'The introduction of yoga in the West has been beautiful. They have started using yoga for the physical and mental benefits it provides. Nothing wrong! I only want people to understand that they can go a few steps further that's all. There is a beautiful story…

One day, there was a woodcutter cutting trees on the outer edge of a forest. An enlightened Master came along and saw the woddcutter. The Master said to the woodcutter, 'go deep.'

So the woodcutter went inside the forest and he found sandalwood. He cut up the sandalwood and immediately started selling it in the market.

The next day, the woodcutter went back and continued to cut up the sandalwood. The Master saw him again and said, 'go deep.' The woodcutter went further inside and found a silver mine. He started mining the silver and started bringing it out to sell to the world.

The man continued to happily mine his silver. The Master came past again and said, 'go deep.' The man went further inside and found

a gold mine! He started mining and selling the gold to the world.

Again, the Master walked past and urged the man to, 'go deep.' The man went yet still further inside and finally found a diamond mine!

Like this, how they have started presenting yoga in the West is beautiful. Nothing wrong! My word is 'go deep.' People can find a lot more through yoga and people can find a lot more through meditation.'

What is Yoga?

When we asked Paramahamsa for his definition of yoga, his answer was;
When we say 'union', it is like an end product which in a sense it is. But that word does not convey the intensity and vibrancy of that ultimate state of existence. So I feel 'uniting' would be a better way of explaining the word yoga. Yes, yoga does not actually mean 'union.' Yoga means 'uniting.' Uniting is a high energy process and one of intense enthusiasm. Conversely, the word 'union' does not have intense

enthusiasm and union is not a process. Yoga means uniting. It's a continuous process and be very clear, the process never ends. Enlightenment is not the end. Enlightenment is the ultimate but it is not the end. Yoga is meant to be the intense

process constantly happening in your Being.'

In modern society, especially in the West, when we consider yoga, we immediately associate it as being a series of yoga *asana* (postures), physically executed to promote strength, flexibility and balance in the body. Yoga is more or less promoted as a physical form of exercise to attain optimum fitness with some breathing techniques and some meditation practices thrown in to maintain its exotic flavor. That's all, nothing more and nothing less. This is like using a precious diamond as a marble!

Paramahamsa says,
'You cannot reduce yoga to a physical exercise. Meditation cannot be reduced to something that can provide you with a little bit of peace. No! These practices have much deeper and sacred meanings.'

Yoga is a great science. It is one of the six basic systems of Indian thought which together are called *darshana*. The word *darshana* is derived from the Sanskrit word *drs* which means 'to see.' This implies that the knowledge of yoga was derived through the process of meditation or internal seeing. It also implies that as a practice, yoga is a tool that we use to look within ourselves, to see where we come from, to realize what we are.

In very broad terms, yoga is a means to unite with our Higher Self. It means to come together and become one in body, mind and spirit. It implies a movement from the outer to the inner. Traditionally, yoga means the union of the *atma* (the individual soul) with the *paramatma* (the universal soul).

Yoga is a complete system that helps each individual achieve his or her full potential. Though its roots are deep in tradition, its outlook is totally contemporary. It beautifully combines ancient wisdom and modern scientific orientation. Yoga is a truly global system. It is a systemized body of knowledge and practice that is inherently flexible. It accepts an individual 'as he is, where he is.' Its appeal is universal as its only interest is to develop the human faculties and integrate the physical, emotional, mental and spiritual aspects of the aspiring individual.

Yoga is a holistic science. It was never confined to being a specific practice but a way of living that impacted every aspect of life. The great sage Patanjali, considered the Father of Yoga, in his extraordinary treatise, the *Yoga Sutra*, emphasizes the total mastery of all aspects of human life the body, the breath, the mind, health and social relationships.

Down the ages, the strength of Patanjali's message encoded in the *sutra*, have been diluted to suit the understandings of those who propagated them. The enormous changes in emerging societies, differing cultures, religions, external influences and limited understandings have reduced the message of Patanjali to a watered down version of its original glory.

Patanjali's Ashtanga Yoga

The core of Patanjali's *Yoga Sutra* has to do with the perception of things and the ways in which our mind loses its pristine clarity, which is its true nature. The aim of yoga practice is to make our perception clearer and through this process bring about a profound transformation within us a transformation that will help us touch base with our Original State, which is *ananda* or bliss.

Patanjali's Yoga has been called variously as *Raja yoga,* or *Ashtanga yoga,* depending from which angle people viewed his teachings. What is of relevance is that all these names are appropriate and applicable. Patanjali speaks about using the eight limbs of yoga (*Ashtanga Yoga*) including body and breath to move into the state of meditation (*Hatha Yoga*) and remain in that state of clarity and awareness at all times (*Raja Yoga*). Due to personal interpretation, reasons of practicality and a culture specific approach, one or the other aspects of Patanjali's Yoga has been highlighted.

Never have the eight limbs been approached together.

Patanjali established the fact that experiencing the ultimate truth of our Original Nature is what yoga practice is all about. Through his terse aphorisms, he brilliantly reveals his vast understanding of the nature of the mind and the obstacles and obstructions that it throws in the path of enlightenment.

What is Patanjali's view of the nature of the mind?

Patanjali's Concept of the Mind

Patanjali's *yoga sutra* is the heart of yoga. It is also the last word on the mind. It is composed of 196 *sutra* or aphorisms. The complete work is divided into four distinct chapters or *padas*:

1) samadhi pada: This *pada* is composed of fifty one *sutras*. In it, Patanjali speaks about the absolute, true consciousness or *Ishvara*. Then, he enumerates the problems an individual is likely to face in his quest to merge with the divine energy.

2) sadhana pada: This *pada* is composed of fifty five *sutras*. It very clearly establishes the nature of yoga and the means through which the *chitta vritti* (mental modifications) can be controlled. It identifies the obstacles to meditation and advocates the practice of *Ashtanga Yoga*.

3) vibhuti pada: This *pada* is composed of fifty six *sutra*. It emphasizes that knowledge is power and gives the techniques for attaining *siddhis* (spiritual powers) and using them for the best possible results. It deals with the subtle state of awareness and advanced techniques.

4) kaivalya pada: This *pada* is composed of thirty four *sutra*. *Kaivalya* means solitariness and detachment. It deals with the effect of our engraved memories and gives the means for erasing such impressions. It describes the yogi who has attained this freedom from all bondages.

The *Yoga Sutra* is a universal treatise because its focus is on the qualities of the mind and the ways in which we can influence it and be influenced by it. When we work at all times with awareness, we influence the mind. On the other hand, when we work unconsciously without awareness, we are influenced by the mind.

Patanjali clearly states that yoga is the tool and the practice to direct the mind without distractions or interruptions. In this book, he addresses the questions about the nature of the mind, which are universal and of interest to all.

In the *Yoga Sutra*, Patanjali uses the word, *avidya* or 'incorrect comprehensions' to describe false perception. On the reverse is *vidya,* which is clarity.

Avidya is the accumulated result of our unconscious ways of perception and behavior. In other words, we see what we want to see, hear what we want to hear and do things according to what we see, hear and think. It is not so much the seeing and hearing that is the root of the problem as much as *how* we see and hear. What is it that makes us see, hear and perceive something in a particular way? What are those things that make us see and act in a habituated manner?

Patanjali says that *avidya* is like a huge tree with many branches. These branches are the obstacles to clarity or *vidya*. They prevent us from seeing things as they really are. These obstacles are *asmita* (ego), *raga* (attachments), *dvesa* (rejection) and *abhinivesha* (fear). All habituated patterns of perceiving the world and behaving according to those perceptions are called *samskara*. They cloud the mind and obstruct the flow of clarity and awareness that is our consciousness.

When we are in this confused state, we experience *dukkha* (generally understood as suffering or sickness). When we are in *dukkha* we feel constricted. *Avidya* and *dukkha* are closely linked to one another. When any action stems from the unconscious or from ignorance, it always leads to suffering.

Patanjali declares that the only goal of yoga is to reduce or remove the cloud from the mind, lessen the *dukkha* and allow the individual to make decisions in the light of conscious awareness. Through a regular practice of yoga, we can remain present in every moment and express our inner nature, the actualization of our inherent potential.

The *yoga sutra* states that the minute we start recognizing the branches of *avidya*, we start to overcome them. There are three ways in which we can do this;

1) tapas deep cleansing techniques, inner purification practices.

'Tapas' has been erroneously understood as penance, denial and rigorous spiritual practices to the point of physical mortification. If we look at the root from which *tapas* comes, '*tap*', we understand it means to heat, to cleanse. In

the yoga context, *tapas* would be those practices that would help us burn our energy blocks and cleanse the impurities within. Through *asana* and *pranayama* we are able to achieve this to a large extent.

2) svadhyaya 'sva' means 'self' and 'adhyaya' means 'the study of', or investigation into the Self.

By focusing on ourselves, we bring in more clarity to our thoughts and actions. We befriend our body; we connect to our breath; we relate better with those around us as we start dropping our tight personal boundaries. Reading inspiring books, listening to the discourses of Masters and engaging in self-learning with like-minded people are all methods of *svadhyaya*.

3) ishvara pranidhana love of Higher Self (God)

This connotes a kind of surrender that goes beyond our mind. It is an expression of the understanding that 'whatever is happening is what is good.' It also means doing our work without bothering about the fruits of our actions.

All these put together with the core practice of *dhyana* help us to enjoy good health, clarity of mind and work with an attitude of surrender.
We can clearly see that from being a complete, total understanding of life where the integration of the body, mind, spirit is of paramount importance, yoga has been reduced to a mere physical practice. A cog in a huge

wheel has been accorded the status of the wheel itself while the wheel has been relegated to the position of the cog!

Why is this happening?

Only a person who has attained the consciousness of Patanjali, who resides in that same inner space as Patanjali can speak authoritatively on Patanjali's teachings. Over a period of time, when more and more teachers, rather than enlightened masters came into contact with the common man, Patanjali's words took precedence over the spirit in which they were taught. With the development of and the importance given to logic and enquiry, Patanjali's verbalization gained importance at the cost of his body language. Many scholars wrote commentaries on the *Yoga Sutra* of Patanjali. All the commentaries are no doubt great scholarly works; but they are dry because they have not woven the fullness of Patanjali's non-verbal, body language into their work. They are not a faithful representation of the spirit of Patanjali's *sutra*.

So what is the most popular and widespread view of Patanjali's Yoga? How do people understand and practice it?

The Prevalent View of Ashtanga Yoga

*A*shtanga Yoga is understood as 8 'steps' of yoga. We practice with the belief that the following practices have to be done one after the other.

1) *yama* (restraints),
2) *niyama* (personal conduct),
3) *asana* (bodily postures),
4) *pranayama* (breathing techniques),
5) *pratyahara* (withdrawal of the senses),
6) *dharana* (single pointed focus),
7) *dhyana* (meditation) and
8) *samadhi* (enlightenment)

The following diagram depicts this clearly:

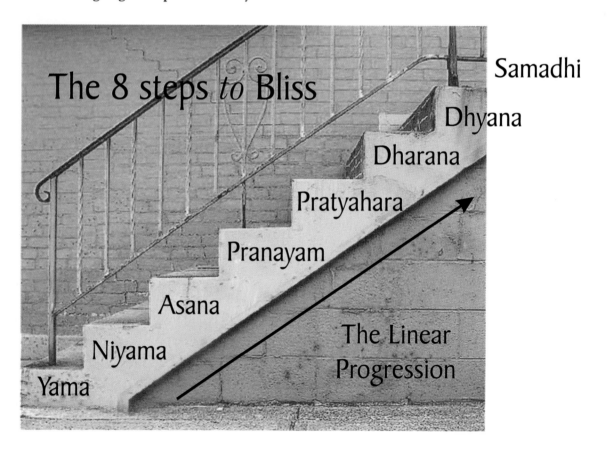

The 8 steps *to* Bliss

Samadhi
Dhyana
Dharana
Pratyahara
Pranayam
Asana
Niyama
Yama

The Linear Progression

Paramahamsa says Patanjali never meant that each step has to be mastered *before* we go to the next step. If that were so we would need several lifetimes to reach the blissful state of *samadhi*. When we see Patanjali's Yoga as progressive steps to enlightenment our mind immediately perceives a goal, which can be reached through hard work over a period of time. So there is a feeling that we need to work hard and that at some future date we will get rewarded for this.

common core. The essence of the core or the center is established in each independent petal.

If we take this core to be the experience of *samadhi*, then every petal or *anga* (part) of the whole flower (*yama, niyama, asana, pranayama, pratyahara, dharana, dhyana*) is by default imbedded with the blissful energy of the state of *samadhi* or Oneness.

It is very clear that *samadhi* is not the eighth step to work towards progressively. On the contrary, it is the state we are already in, the state of *nithya ananda*, Eternal Bliss. It just need to expressed.

When that expression happens, intensely, moment to moment, our consciousness flowers and we are in Nithya Yoga; Eternal Uniting.

Patanjali was the first Master who created a

Paramahamsa declares that Patanjali never intended *ashtanga yoga* to be practiced this way. This copper flower (seen in photo above) is a part of Patanjali's *samadhi* (tomb) in Rameshwaram, South India. It symbolic of the spirit of *Ashtanga Yoga*.

There is a center with seven independent petals attached to it. Though the petals are independent, their very contact points connect them to one another. They share the same

clear, scientific and logical system to reproduce the experience of enlightenment. Prior to Patanjali, enlightenment was an accident; it was a gamble, with no guarantee. Patanjali was the first master and spiritual navigator responsible for the mapping of consciousness and codifying complete directions. He created an exact formula to reproduce the experience of enlightenment; just as how scientists create formulae to reproduce experiences of the outer world, Patanjali created a beautiful formula and technology to reproduce the experience of the inner world.

Paramahamsa says, *'There are two types of scientists. Scientists of the outer world and scientists of the inner world. Scientists of the outer world are those who create formulas to reproduce the outer world experiences. Scientists of the inner world are those who create formulas to reproduce experiences of the inner world - in others. Patanjali was one such inner scientist. He created a formula, 8 yogic practices that would reproduce in others the inner space of Patanjali himself.'*

Many masters and teachers of the yoga tradition have added to the understanding of yoga. They have enriched the experiencing of yoga with their unique insights into the teaching and practice. All of them agree that modern man is a complex phenomenon reflecting the enormous changes that have taken place in the last century. This being so, old-fashioned, incomplete methods of integrating the body, mind and spirit are ineffective today. Bullock cart methods of teaching are for the bullock cart age. Jet age methods are required for the jet age.

Patanjali's samadhi (tomb) at Ramanatha Swamy Temple, Rameshwaram, Southern India. The copper flower expresses the spirit of yoga, as expressed by Patanjali.

The Need of the Hour

Over time as cultures changed and inner pollution increased, emphasis on Patanjali's Yoga system changed into what was acceptable. Patanjali's body language was completely forgotten. Humanity has stayed true to the words; the spirit has been shrouded in unconscious obscurity.

The state of the body and the quality of the mind has undergone radical changes. Our lifestyle, the way in which we sit, move and work, the types of food we eat and the kind of information we are exposed to have all combined together to make us very different from our ancestors.

The modern mind has an attention span of not more than 3 seconds. To work with the body seems much easier than to work with the mind. We are more comfortable with things at a grosser, material level than at the subtle, spiritual level. Modern man needs the model of the human mind that will be easy to understand and relate with. Also, we need a practice that will be quick, direct and deeply effective.

So what we need is an approach to the practice of yoga that is straight, effective and brings about individual transformation rapidly; an approach that will bring back to life the lost body-language of the great Patanjali himself.

That approach is already here.

Paramahamsa, the young, inner scientist and Master of the present age, has a profound understanding of the human mind. With a deep reverence for Patanjali, he re-presents the earlier view of the mind in a direct, modern and elegant manner. He resurrects the lost language of Patanjali's very Being. He brings to vibrant life the body language expressed by the great sage himself.

Paramahamsa conducting an advanced level meditation program in Los Angeles, California.

The Nithyananda Sutra: 'Be Un-clutched'

'We are nothing but a collection of unconnected, independent, illogical thoughts. By our very nature we are 'un-clutched'.'

- *Paramahamsa*

The new understanding

'Be un-clutched' is the experience, expression and the teaching of the enlightened Master, Paramahamsa Nithyananda. Paramahamsa states emotions and thoughts give birth to our mental set up and attitude. Understanding the play of emotions and thoughts is the first and final step towards moving beyond it. He declares that man by his very nature is an un-clutched and blissful Being.

What do we mean by the term un-clutched?

Every thought that arises in us is like a bubble that forms, rises and dies. Every thought independently rises and dies before the next thought comes up. For example, if you are sitting in a chair and suddenly get up, the moment you have decided to get up, that moment the thought of sitting has left you. If you are working on your computer and decide to shut down the machine, that moment, the thought that you want to work has died. Every thought is unconnected and happens in a series, one after the other. One thought has to die before the next one comes up. This is our true nature.

Like bubbles in a fish tank our thoughts too are separate, distinct and unconnected. When these bubbles slowly rise, one after the other, no connectivity is seen. It is clear that they are all independent bubbles. On the other hand, when the bubbles are rising very fast and are many in number, they project the illusion of being connected to one another. They appear to solidify into a pattern.

Similarly, when there are too many thoughts

within us, all seemingly happening at the same time, the illusion of connectivity happens. We start believing we are these connections.

Our true nature is to renounce thoughts every passing moment; to allow each thought to rise like a bubble and burst and allow the next thought to rise. Our thoughts have only a vertical existence, like rising bubbles.

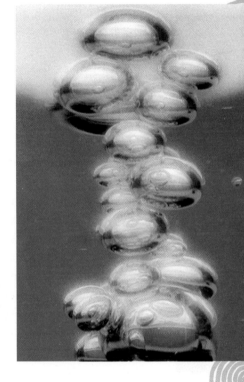

This process of allowing thoughts to rise and die without trying to connect them is what we mean by being un-clutched. As long as this natural process is allowed to happen, things are alright.

However, what we do is start connecting our thoughts randomly and forming a shaft. For example, the suffering, pain or depression that we had 10 years ago, 9 years ago, 8 years ago or 7 years ago are all independent and unconnected incidents. These experiences of emotional and physical pain happened for different reasons, in different situations, in different times and spaces. However, mentally, for our own personal reference and convenience we tend to archive all of these experiences of pain in one individual file. Next we start believing that these independent and unconnected experiences are actually connected. Therefore, we naturally come to the conclusion that our life was nothing but pain, suffering and depression. When we start believing that this shaft is a representation of our past, we expect that our future too will be similar. This very conditioning ultimately plays a major role in creating and designing our life.

By doing this, we convert the vertical and un-clutched process into a horizontal one with linear connectivity. Here starts the whole problem. All thoughts with like-energies (similarly associated energies) are collected, clutched and made into a shaft. For example, all painful memories when gathered together create a pain-shaft. Similarly, all pleasurable memories when clutched together create a pleasure-shaft. We must understand that both these shafts are an illusion. They do not exist. They are unconnected incidents that are sewn together. They never existed in that form. They are a creation of the mind, which by itself is a myth, an illusion. Therefore, we are living an illusion within an illusion.

As long as each thought is allowed to rise and die, we can take on any amount of load at the physical and mental planes and our consciousness will remain light and blissful. Once we start connecting the thoughts, our consciousness suffers and we start feeling burdened. It becomes damaging to our Being. The true nature of our mind is nothing but unconnected, illogical, independent and un-clutched thoughts. However, since the mind operates in time, we develop an illusion of the past and the future. We forget that all we actually have is the present moment, which is essentially timeless.

All emotions like worry, lust, discontentment, jealousy, fear, ego and attention-need are purely because we find a connection between independent incidents, between independent thoughts and create a concept for ourselves and start relating with that concept. We create an imaginary shaft with our thoughts and we suffer because of this.

It is these emotions that create all forms of violence be it religious wars, social conflicts or political unrest. The basis or the root of all forms of violence is our emotions and the basis of our emotions is our habit of creating imaginary shafts of our thoughts and empowering them to work on us.

The main thing we do while creating these shafts is, we choose the thoughts depending on whether we want pain or pleasure. We pick pleasant thoughts at random and connect them to form a shaft of pleasure or pick negative thoughts and connect them to form a shaft of pain. We create shafts of pain and pleasure alternately for ourselves and keep oscillating between these two emotions.

To un-clutch from this shaft, whether of pain or pleasure is the master key to a blissful life.

If we deeply analyze how we connect our thoughts instead of renouncing them, we will understand how we create suffering for ourselves. It is the mind that finds the connection. As such, there is no connection between our thoughts.

We have been trained to feed on words and thoughts. That is why we create these shafts. We feed on words because we operate out of fear or greed all the time. Out of fear or greed, we create connectivity in our thoughts. We are afraid to let go of this process because if we let go, there is nothing else to hold on to. We have never experienced an un-clutched state of mind where there is no shaft; there are only bubble-like thoughts, each independent of the other.

In the un-clutched state, there is no scope for fear or greed. We will simply *be*, that's all. It is a dimension that we rarely experience because we are so used to clutching onto the familiar shaft of thoughts.

Here is a small story to illustrate this point...

An eye specialist was treating a blind man. He assured him, 'Once I operate on your eye, you will have your vision back and you can throw your stick away.' The blind man became afraid when he heard this. He asked the doctor, "I understand that I will get my vision, but how can I walk without my stick?'

The man was so used to walking with the stick that he could not understand that by getting his vision he can throw away the stick!

In the same way, when the truth is that we can live in an un-clutched fashion blissfully, we wonder how we can be without clutching onto the shaft of thoughts. We see it as something natural, something inevitable!

We fail to see how mythical the whole thing is. Our mind is a myth. We have empowered it and become a slave to it. It is nothing but mental slavery.

Just watch the thoughts rising in you. Clearly see how each thought rises and dies and the next thought comes up. Observe how you effortlessly connect these thoughts and create ideas and concepts. Watch the play of these concepts upon yourself; you will understand how you create the whole myth.

Be un-clutched

Connecting thoughts is the original sin. That moment of connecting is the fall from grace. It is at that time when spirit becomes solid matter; God becomes man; cosmic space is reduced to individual ego.

Living in an un-clutched fashion is the only way to blissful living. Just decide that you will not connect any two thoughts, that you will not pass any judgment on any thought or any incident. The moment you find yourself connecting, simply un-clutch from it. Keep on un-clutching every time you remember this technique; your mental setup will automatically be transformed.

When we work in an un-clutched fashion, we will find our capacity expanding; we can take on a lot more responsibility without getting stressed; we will not experience mood swings between pain and pleasure; we will be blissful all the time. We are so used to happiness that comes with a reason. This reason is again a shaft that we create with our thoughts. Once we stop creating these shafts, we will be blissful all the time. We will actualize our hidden potential and realize the ultimate truth; we are nothing less than God!

The term un-clutched, does not mean that we should be aloof and cold to people and situations around us. We just shouldn't connect

our thoughts and start the process of creating shafts, that's all.

We should remember that we are beautiful and un-clutched Beings by nature; that is enough. We will stop creating misery for ourselves and for others.

When we are dwelling in the past, or focusing on the future we miss out on the present. If we observe our thoughts we can experience the deafening noise of our inner chatter. It becomes obvious that our thoughts are furiously oscillating between the past and the future. The speed at which they move is so fast that we fail to realize that there is a gap, however small, between the end of one thought and the beginning of another. That gap is the present moment. We never seem to pause, let alone remain in the present. What we need to internalize is that energy is available only in the 'now', in the present moment. This constant jumping from the past to the future does not allow us to access energy. We are always in *want*.

How can our energy levels be increased? How do we stop the continuous noise of this inner chatter? How can we bring sanity to this madness? How can we widen the gap between thoughts and dwell in that silent space which is our true nature?

Is there a practical way to experience the Nithyananda *sutra*: 'Be Un-clutched'?

Paramahamsa says there is a way; 'Once we understand how the mind works, the potential power in our Being will be simply unleashed. We will walk like Gods on planet Earth.'

The Modern Mind and How it Works

'Our mind is our major dilemma'

- Paramahamsa

Paramahamsa states that as long as the mind is the servant and we are the masters, all is well. The minute we give power to the mind to become our master, then the confusion starts. All the energy gets imbalanced within us and leads to a state of *dukkha,* dis-ease.

What is this energy all about?

According to the Vedic understanding, the human being has seven energy bodies of which the physical is the grossest. Of these seven, the first three are relevant to us. The first is the physical body or *jagrat shareera*. This is the body that moves, talks, writes and carries on with similar activities.

Next comes the dream body, *sukshma shareera*. This is the body we use to move from place to place in our dreams.

The third is the *karana shareera*, which we use when we are in deep sleep. This body does not move.

The second and the third bodies, (*sukshma* and *karana shareera*) meet the physical body (*jagrat shareera*) at seven places along the length of the physical body. These seven points are known as the *chakra*, which are spinning wheels or vortices of energy. There are seven major *chakra* and a number of minor ones, but the seven major ones are responsible for our physical and mental well being.

These *chakra* were discovered by the Vedic seers thousands of years ago. Medical science has proven that there is an endocrine gland that corresponds to each of these seven *chakra*. Together they are responsible for maintaining the homeostasis of the body.

Chakra are boundless energy centers. They are not physical entities in our body. They are metaphysical representations as they belong to the auric body. Kirlian photography has enabled us to capture these *chakra* and prove their existence.

Chakra are very intimately connected to our emotions. Whenever we experience a particular emotion, depending on whether it is positive or negative, the *chakra* will expand or contract accordingly. When we are functioning at an optimal level, the size of the *chakra* is that of a cartwheel; otherwise, it shrinks to the size of a coat button.

These seven major *chakra* deeply influence our physical, emotional and mental activities. They have great power. They are energy centers which, when cleansed and energized, empower us to experience the seemingly impossible. We then lead a vibrant and blissful life.

Our dis-ease is only an imbalance in any one of these *chakra* because our body and mind is very deeply rooted in our inner consciousness. By keeping these *chakra* in a healthy state we can see a transformation happening in us at the physical and mental levels.

The state of our mind plays a major role in how we perceive the world and in turn how we view ourselves. Our perception in turn determines our energy levels, which in turn is responsible for deciding whether the *chakra* are blocked or opened.

So what is the role of the mind in blocking the energy from flowing into our system?

If being un-clutched is our original nature how do we lose it?

How we Perceive

We see what we want to see, we hear what we want to hear and our attitude and behavior gets shaped by our perception of the world. So how do we perceive the world? What are the mechanics behind the perceptual process?

The following diagram shows us the mechanics of the mind and how it influences our perceptions.

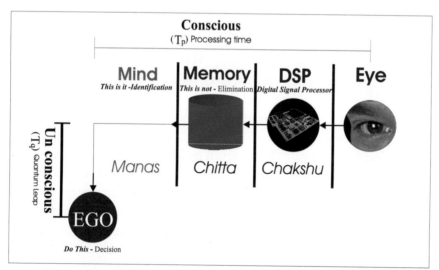

How the mind works

Everything we perceive is taken in through all of our five senses. The diagram above shows how the information that enters through our eyes is processed. It is representative of all other senses too. However, for purpose of clarity we are using the sense of seeing as the example to illustrate this process.

When we see something, first the eye sees it. The eye is merely a camera, which faithfully records the outside world. The energy that sees is not the eye. This energy is called *chakshu* in Sanskrit. The nature of this energy is to digitize the information seen by the eye. It is something like a digital signal processor (DSP). The signal or the input is converted into a digital file by the *chakshu*. It has to be understood that this conversion happens to the information received through all the five senses, not just the eye.

This file goes to the memory (*chitta*). In the memory, the work of analyzing the information begins. This is done through the process of elimination, 'It is not this, it is not this.' Identification does not occur here. For example, when we see the yoga teacher in front of us, this information is taken up by the digital signal processor and passed onto the memory. The memory does not identify the object in front of the eye as a yoga teacher, rather it says what '*it is not*'. For example, it says, 'This is not an animal, this is not a tree' and so on. The identification of the fact that it is a yoga teacher standing in front of us does not happen here.

Then the file goes to the mind (*manas*). It is the mind that does the job of identifying the information. It says 'this is a yoga teacher.' Unlike the memory which says, '*this is not*,' the mind concludes, '*this is it*'.

Next, the entire file takes a quantum leap to the ego and our ego decides our next action or decision based on our past experience. If we have had past experiences with yoga teachers that have been pleasing and beneficial, we will decide to practice yoga again with a teacher. If, on the other hand, we have not had a pleasant experience in a yoga class, we will take the decision to leave the class.

Try to understand this process. We see the yoga teacher. The eye passes the information to the digital signal processor, which in turn passes it to the memory, which does the job of eliminating unwanted information. Then the memory passes this reduced information to the mind, which does the job of identification. Then the whole file takes a quantum leap to the ego, which makes the decision based on our past experiences.

The time for the process between the eye and the mind is logical and conscious. It happens with our complete awareness but at great speed.

The time for the quantum leap from the mind to the ego is mostly unconscious. It happens without our awareness.

Why does this happen? Why do we decide unconsciously and regret later?

Mind operating through Instinct, Intellect or Intuition

The reason is this unconscious zone is filled with negative memories and restlessness. All of our past memories (*samskara*), all our past thought patterns are stored in this zone as files. Psychologists use the word 'engram' to describe these deeply engraved memories. There are many of these files stored in this zone without any logical connections between them.

Because of the great clutter in this unconscious zone, the file does not even reach the ego for a proper decision to be made. On the other hand, these stored engrams play upon the information that is received. They just impose themselves and cause havoc in the decision making process.

As a result, the ego makes a quick and hasty decision, purely at the instinctual level and passes the file back. All this happens unconsciously at lightning speed.

This unconscious area is very powerful. It is a great storehouse of latent energy and can be used in three ways:

1) Instinctual level
2) Intellectual level
3) Intuitive level

As long as the unconscious is overloaded with deep restlessness and negative memories, it always works at the instinct level. All decisions are taken unconsciously and instinctively. That is why, during moments of clarity, we always end up regretting most of our decisions.
We wonder, 'Why did I behave in that fashion? This is not me! How did I allow this to happen?'

Our unclear decisions occur when the time taken to go to the ego and back is very short in comparison to the time taken for the process between the eye and the mind. In other words, we are operating at the instinct level.

At the intellectual level, we are conscious, we make decisions logically but we don't have any extra enthusiasm or energy. We are not creative or innovative; we don't take big steps and we don't grow. We are in a break-even state. We don't make hasty decisions out of restlessness or overloading of our unconscious zone but we are still not using our potential to the extent that it can be maximized.

The next level, the level of intuition is the zone wherein we can actualize our entire potential. Engraved memories can ultimately be removed if we infuse a deep silence and awareness into the unconscious zone. When we can be free from our memories, we are empty and blissful. It is then that we become alive and fresh every moment without the burden of our past, which is nothing but the weight of the engraved memories. When this happens, the energy of our Being expresses itself in its purest form. We experience our true nature, which is eternal bliss, *nithya ananda*. We realize that we are nothing lesser than God!

When we are in the intuitive level, all our decisions will be spontaneous, taken from the energy of our intuition, from deep awareness, peace and bliss. We simply *know* with tremendous clarity all that is to be known. We don't know the steps that have led us to our conclusions, but we know for sure that our conclusions or decisions are right. Intuition not only gives us the energy to make decisions but also the energy to act on these decisions. We are absolutely confident and brimming with energy and are in no doubt whatsoever regarding the decisions we make. This is the power of operating at all times from the level of intuition. The potential, which is inside our Being, is completely unleashed. If we recognize and encourage this, we can express the higher dimensions of our Being.

Intuition is the energy of our Being. When this pure energy starts coming out from the unconscious level, it also heals us physically, mentally and emotionally. Apart from healing it reduces stress and helps us take decisions spontaneously.

When intuition happens beyond our intellect, our whole being is integrated, comes together harmoniously. This is experiencing the meaning of yoga, union. Yogis have said again and again that when we operate from the level of intuition, we are at our peak. Accessing this level is what inner science is all about.

To most of us, intuitive people are classified as special or gifted. What we need to understand and what the great mystics of the inner world have repeatedly stated is that we *also* can have it.

When we make meditation the thread that ties together the various aspects of yoga, simultaneous integration happens. Then intuition becomes an integral part of our regular life. It will be the preferred mode of communication.

Yoga is the best method for an integrated approach to life. The practice of *asana, pranayama* and meditation together, act as a powerful, cleansing and energizing agent. What we need to realize is that unless we practice yoga in this integrated, wholesome manner, we cannot expect any kind of deep and lasting benefits from it.

Yoga is not just for the body alone. If viewed in this manner, we reduce the profound to the mundane.

Nithya Yoga as developed by Paramahamsa is a completely new approach to the teaching of yoga. In it are combined the wisdom of ancient traditions and the investigative spirit of modern science. Though its roots are in classical yoga, its methodology and presentation are totally revolutionary.

Nithya Yoga

'When the ultimate uniting happens, intensely, moment to moment, it is eternal; it is Nithya Yoga'.

- *Paramahamsa*

Introduction to Nithya Yoga

express and radiate that state, a little preparation is needed.'

The whole purpose of Nithya Yoga is to help people un-clutch and experience eternal bliss. It is the simple and straightforward path of enlightenment. It is not a methodology to experience physical and mental well-being; they are mere by-products.

Nithya Yoga is not just a 'feel good' 90 minute practice session which is divorced from the rest of the day's activities. It is that time that we give ourselves to learn something more about the quality of our nature. We identify our likes and dislikes, our ingrained habits, our comfort zones and the way in which we deal with the challenges in life. When we practice Nithya Yoga with full awareness such a profound inner knowing will happen within us. We will realize that we can learn so much about ourselves and use this learning to bring about a total transformation at a personal and interpersonal level. This is what yoga is all about…Self knowledge.

Nithya Yoga is a direct method expressed by Paramahamsa, that will prepare the body and mind to experience, sustain and express the energy of enlightenment.

Paramahamsa says, *'To have a glimpse of pure consciousness, for one to have one satori (no mind state) is not such a big thing; anyone can have. But to stay in that space and to*

The methodology of the Nithya Yoga practice has the inherent capacity to cleanse us of our suppressed emotional blocks and deeply embedded *samskaras*.

In order to avoid the pitfalls of modern living, it is essential to energize one's *chakra*, the energy centers, and to dissolve one's *samskaras*.

Our education system, our upbringing and our lifestyle does not allow for an integrated balanced growth. Surprisingly, right from a very young age we are taught everything that does not allow for the expression of our inherent energy. We are self-centered but in a negative way. Selfishness, discontentment, jealousy, comparison, fantasy and an exaggerated idea of who we are has always been encouraged and rewarded in our society. Therefore, all our energy centers become blocked. We always feel a lack within us. We are not ready to receive yoga in its true essence.

In Patanjali's era, people generally led a life that naturally kept these suppressions low; but not any more. Our modern educational systems promote negative thinking, raise our *samskaras* which in turn block our *chakra*. We are taught so much about the outside world but hardly anything about ourselves and our connectivity to everything around us. The lifestyle that we follow is competitive rather than collaborative. Therefore we are prone to a stressful way of living.

In a Nithya Yoga class, we address this primarily by incorporating a revolutionary meditation technique that Paramahamsa has formulated called *Nithya Dhyaan* (Life Bliss Meditation).

Yoga has never been simpler or more effective!

All that Patanjali taught is now available to us in its purest essence in one simple unique package called Nithya Yoga.

In Patanjali's days, the *gurukulam* system of education created integrated human beings. The development of all aspects, body/mind/spirit, was given equal importance and led to balanced growth. In such a scenario, there was not much need for any technique of cleansing to be taught. Their very lifestyle and their education took care of that. They were ready to practice yoga in its purest form.

Many might believe that Nithya Yoga is just another 'new' system of yoga that is surfacing in the world of yoga. Actually, Nithya Yoga is the most ancient system as Patanjali had originally taught. Nithya Yoga is bringing back to life, the essence of Patanjali, because through the passage of time his teaching and its original purpose has been completely lost and mis-represented to the world.

The Lost Body Language

Paramahamsa's teacher, Raghupati yogi mastered the whole science. Not only the physical aspects of yoga, the *asana* or *hatha yoga*, but also all other aspects of yoga. He worked with *prana*, worked with the mind, worked with visualization power and with emotions and had deep insights into the core truth.

Raghupati yogi's insights were revealing and sometimes shocking. Many times, his insights even looked very contradictory to what Patanjali originally recorded in the *Yoga Sutra*.

Paramahamsa would ask Raghupati yogi, 'I am able to understand what Patanjali writes in the *Yoga Sutra* but I am unable to understand your commentary.' Raghupati yogi would reply to him in a beautiful way; he would say, 'In all the books that you have seen and read, even in the *Yoga Sutra*, only the verbal language of Patanjali is recorded, but not Patanjali's body language. What he originally wanted to convey is not recorded, therefore, naturally much has been lost.'

This is a profound statement that needs to be understood very clearly. We can explain with the following example.

Paramahamsa now speaks about being un-clutched. When he speaks in front of an audience, He will say, 'be un-clutched.' Fortunately we have a video recorder and we are able to visually record everything that Paramahamsa speaks. We can record all that he is say's and the purpose for which he is saying it. The video recording also captures his body language, ambience and energy in which he is expressing his teachings. Patanjali's teachings were never recorded in this way. So obviously, the essence, the ambience in which he conveyed his teachings and the core message of his teachings have been misinterpreted and lost over time.

If we only took Paramahamsa's verbal or written message and convey it to the next generation, after 200 years only the words, 'be un-clutched' will be delivered. Only his words will be delivered and not his body language, which always conveys so much.

If someone asks in 200 years time, 'What was the message of Paramahamsa Nithyananda?' The other person, who is supposed to be an authority on his teachings may say, 'He always used to say, 'be un-clutched'. The enquiring person will think, 'Oh, to 'be un-clutched' means I should not drive anything with clutches; I must stop driving cars!' Then the other person will say, 'You must not only stop driving cars, anything which clutches should not be used! That is the meaning of Paramahamsa's teachings!'

You all must have played the game of Chinese whispers sometime in your lives. You start with a phrase, whisper it to the next person, then that person whispers it to the next and so on. By the time you reach the final person, and they speak the phrase out loud, the phrase, more often than not, is completely and utterly different to the phrase spoken at the beginning. It doesn't even come close to the original phrase. This is what happens with words. Even written words that were recorded over 5000 years ago; the message becomes distorted.

The purpose for which be-unclutched has been uttered and the kind of interpretation it will be given after 100 or 200 years we can never know, because only the verbal language will be transmitted, not the body language. If these video recordings are lost, the purpose for which the word is uttered will not be conveyed to the learners and the listeners. Unless they have a person with them who has experienced the truth of being unclutched, who dwells in the state of *nithya ananda*, future generations will catch the words and forget the spirit behind those words.

Similarly, only a person who has experienced the consciousness of Patanjali can bring Patanjali back to life.

Paramahamsa had the great fortune to be with a yogi, Raghupati yogi, who had experienced the consciousness or the same inner space of Patanjali. That is the reason he used to reveal all the deeper level truths of yoga science which seemed very contradictory to all that was been written and taught. As a young boy, Paramahamsa used to argue with him a lot. Whenever he used to ask for a clear cut, logical explanation for some of the things Raghupati yogi used to reveal, the yogi would calmly say, 'that is how it is'. He never fed Paramahamsa's mind more than what it needed. He was interested in making him experience the truth himself.

Nithya Yoga is about imbibing the body language of Patanjali; going beyond his verbalization. By catching the words of Patanjali we have lost the spirit of yoga. Because of the wrong perception of ourselves, we see life as a suffering. Through the practice of Nithya Yoga, we are journeying on a great inner adventure, which will at every given moment uncover the truth of who we really are Nithyananda, Eternal Bliss.

The Deeper Truths of Yoga Revealed

'Nithya Yoga is not the path TO bliss.
Nithya Yoga is the path OF bliss'

                         - Paramahamsa

Paramahamsa says let us look at what Patanjali wanted to convey. Let us first analyze the word yoga. In Sanskrit, the word yoga literally means to unite or to become one with.

Again and again, all the Eastern mystics have declared that **we are energy**! The body is not just a bio- mechanism as we think. Our body is an expression of energy. In the Eastern system, we call the body *'annamaya kosha'*, which is a sheath or outer shell of the energy. We are Energy. We are something more than what we think we are.

Having a direct experience or communion with that energy is what is called yoga. We are not human beings striving for a spiritual experience but we are spiritual beings having the human experience.

The 'path *to* ecstasy' implies that right now we are not in bliss and that we need to work towards ecstasy. So, ecstasy is a state that we need to strive for, a goal we need to achieve, a destination we need to reach. 'We need to be in' means 'as of now, we are not'.

The 'path *of* ecstasy' means the very journey itself is ecstasy. There is no implication here that we are in want or lack something or that we need to strive towards some end. There is no goal to be achieved or destination to be reached. Although we might not realize completely, we are already in ecstasy and we are journeying in ecstasy. Nithya Yoga is all about experiencing and deepening the understanding of this truth.

Nithya Yoga simply translated would mean 'eternal union'. Eternal means past, present *and* future. The one thing that is 'eternal' is the truth of our nature, which is *ananda* or bliss. Every moment that we experience and express this, we are in total, complete 'union' with this bliss. When this happens continuously and expresses itself constantly, we experience 'eternal uniting'…*nithya yoga.*

Bliss Is Our Nature and Our Birthright

What is the authority on which this statement is made?

Paramahamsa says that every baby that comes into this world is an expression of this blissful state of meditation. Newborn babies come into this world with a high level of consciousness but through societal conditionings, upbringing and lifestyle we pollute their state of pure awareness.

Children, as they grow up, will constantly be expressing their natural state of bliss. They are more or less in ecstasy. We observe them spinning around, we see them dancing and jumping all over the place. They laugh and giggle for no obvious reason at all. As adults, we suppress their joy. They are told, 'Don't spin!' 'Stop jumping!' 'Stop laughing!' 'Be quiet!' We have somehow forgotten this natural energy, this naturally uninhibited, blissful state that we all expressed as a child and still *have* within us. It

is, however, lost under all the suppression and conditionings we also received as a child. According to the *Upanishads*, the oldest treatise on spirituality, we have five sheaths termed as *kosha* in Sanskrit. These five sheaths encase our *atman*, our Self. They are in order of subtlety:

1) **annamaya kosha** (physical body),
2) **pranamaya kosha** (pranic body),
3) **manomaya kosha** (mental body),
4) **vijnanamaya kosha** (knowledge body) and finally;
5) **anandamaya kosha** (bliss body).

The presence of the *anandamaya kosha* (bliss body) is further proof of the fact that our very nature is bliss. It exists within us. It is always there. However, it is more or less an aspect of us, which has become remote and completely forgotten.

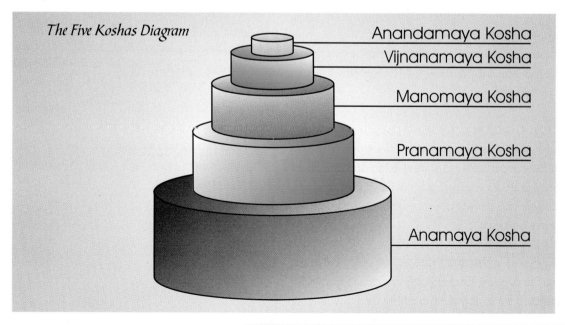

The Five Koshas Diagram

Anandamaya Kosha
Vijnanamaya Kosha
Manomaya Kosha
Pranamaya Kosha
Anamaya Kosha

Additionally, we are composed of seven bodies and they are: the physical body, the *pranic*, the etheric, the spiritual, the causal, the cosmic and at our core is the nirvanic body.

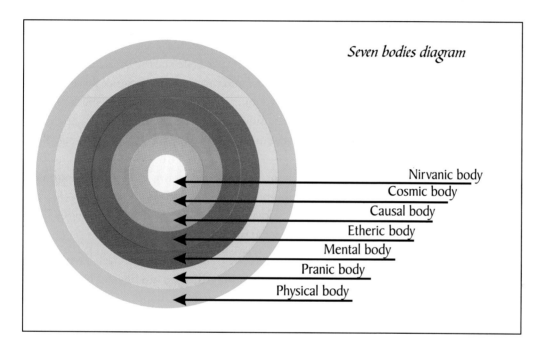

Seven bodies diagram

Nirvanic body
Cosmic body
Causal body
Etheric body
Mental body
Pranic body
Physical body

The final *nirvanic* body is that of total uniting or expansive oneness with the divine consciousness that is within us.

The final authority on the concept that our very nature is bliss is the authority given by the masters. All of the masters down the ages, from every culture and religion emphasize that by our very nature we *are* bliss. Rarely do all masters agree on the same thing because each spiritual master expresses their own individual experience in a unique way. The expressions of Buddha, Krishna and Jesus are different, however, their experiences are one and the same and that experience is one of bliss.

In its present state our body-mind system is not capable of staying in the exalted state of ecstasy. Too much inner pollution due to social conditionings, faulty habits and incorrect perceptions has weakened our capacity to receive the high voltage energy of ecstasy. The modern scientific, materialistic, competitive, achievement oriented lifestyle has led to a total disconnection with our inner self. We have become imbalanced in our development and growth. Through Nithya Yoga the sincere seeker will be prepared not only to experience bliss but also to express it in all aspects of life.

Ashtanga Yoga does not mean eight 'steps'. It means eight 'parts'

The aim of Nithya Yoga is to teach us how to use the tools given by Patanjali in the most effective way. How to groom our body-mind to experience, sustain and express the energy of enlightenment.

The modern mind demands a modern approach.

One of the important teachings that Raghupati yogi expressed to Paramahamsa was that Patanjali's *Ashtanga Yoga* was never meant to be practiced in a step by step, linear progression. Over the years, many have misinterpreted *Ashtanga Yoga* as being a step by step process, whereby a practitioner must master one step before attempting the next step.

Patanjali has used the word *ashta-anga* (8 limbs), not *ashta-pati* (8 steps). He has done this with a purpose. All 8 limbs have to come together *simultaneously* for progress to happen. Science and spirituality, matter and energy are like the two legs of one body. If only one leg is developed at the cost of the other, then there will be lopsided growth. Therefore, a typical Nithya Yoga class is structured in such a way that we work on all eight limbs simultaneously.

Paramahamsa states that if one were to practice *Ashtanga Yoga* in this linear progression, it may take the practitioner lifetimes to reach the final outcome; the eighth step *samadhi* (bliss).

Samadhi is not an end result. *Samadhi* is not an explosion of bliss that happens to a favored few. In very simple terms, whenever we live with awareness in the moment, totally and completely absorbed in whatever we are doing, we are in *samadhi*. For example, whether cooking, writing, studying, playing with our kids, dancing or whatever, we are in the present moment. We are in the 'now', which is the only thing that is truly available to us. During such moments, we experience this state of *samadhi* or bliss. When this state is a continuous 24/7, 365 day experience we call it enlightenment.

In a Nithya Yoga class, instead of practicing with the understanding that *samadhi* or bliss is some far off goal we have to work hard to attain, the minute we walk into our class and center ourselves, we start with the idea that we are bliss and throughout the session, we deepen this understanding that we are bliss. Every technique employed in a Nithya Yoga class is practiced with this strong understanding. This has a tremendous effect on our unconscious zone. Faulty perceptions are cleared, engraved memories are melted and energy blocks are removed. There is a complete harmonious flow in what we think, perceive and do.

When we start our practice with the understanding that we are blissful by nature, a deep transformation happens within us. We change our perception from seeing ourselves as lacking in energy or in a state of dis-ease to realizing ourselves as vibrant, blissful energy sources. Therefore, 'we are bliss' becomes our very experience and expression.

We start with the body and link it to the mind, through the breath. When we do the postures *(asana)* with the appropriate breathing *(pranayama)*, our focus is simultaneously on the breathing and the movement to the exclusion of all else *(pratyahara)*. The mind is turned inward and establishes contact with the breath *(dharana)*. When the mind continues to deepen this activity, meditation *(dhyana)* happens. When it becomes completely absorbed in the whole flow, we experience bliss *(samadhi)*.

The Original Understanding of Yama and Niyama

Normally, *yama* (restraints) and *niyama* (personal conduct) are taken as the first two steps of the traditional linear model of yoga. Paramahamsa says that if one decided to master *yama* and only then move onto the second step, they would never be able to move onto the second step. *Yama* includes truthfulness. Paramahamsa says that no one can ever master truth until you realize and experience the 8th step of *samadhi* or bliss. *Yama* and *niyama* actually happen as a flowering. They are no longer disciplines that need to be forced on us, but attitudes and behaviors that arise out of the experiencing of *ananda* or bliss.

The five restraints (yama) include:

1) Non-violence (*ahimsa*):

Non violence has always been taught to us as a morality. No morality can actually be practiced. When we have a morality imposed on us, we begin practicing it out of fear or greed. Ultimately we only end up troubled and depressed. Paramahamsa says, 'Morality should not be based on our conscience which is societal but it should arise from our consciousness, which is spiritual.' Practicing non-violence should not be imposed as a law. Naturally, if there is a law, it is there to be broken!

When we practice the limbs of yoga simultaneously with the understanding that 'we are bliss', the practice of non-violence becomes a natural expression of this blissful state. We simply fall in tune with our true essence. How can we inflict violence on anything, anyone, or on ourselves when we experience our innate bliss?

2) Truthfulness (*satya*):

The truth has 3 dimensions;

i) Speaking the truth
ii) Thinking the truth
iii) Living the truth

Anyone can speak the truth but only a person who has the courage to live in awareness can think, speak and live the same truth, without any kind of editing or distortion.

During the practice of Nithya Yoga, we experience the understanding that we are by our very nature, *sat-chit-ananda* (truth-consciousness-bliss). Over time, our mind begins to realize this as truth. Finally, we begin to express this truth in our everyday life. Then, automatically there will be no gap between what we think, feel and say. All the three aspects will become a harmonious flow. There will be no need for editing. We will effortlessly speak, think and live all of our truths.

3) Non-stealing (*asteya*):

When do we steal? When we feel that someone else has that which we want but which we do not have or not to the extent that we desire, we are tempted to steal. Stealing is not merely limited to taking away a physical possession belonging to someone else. It can also include taking away their personal space and energy.

Additionally, if someone confides in us and we share a person's information with some other, we're stealing away that person's trust. We are stealing that space that has been entrusted to us.

If we look upon stealing as some rule we can't break, simply our minds look for opportunities to break it. Most of the times, when we make a decision to steal, it is usually a rash, unaware decision made from our unconscious. These decisions are made in the level of instinct.

When we practice yoga with complete awareness, we begin to operate from intuition. We are filled with a blissful peace. We experience a fullness that wipes away all sense of lack. We are never in want. So, non-stealing happens naturally. It is not a law imposed on us that needs to be obeyed out of fear of punishment.

4) Celibacy (*brahmacharya*):

Commonly, when we hear the word *brahmacharya,* immediately we associate it with the practice of celibacy. '*Nothing could be further from the truth,*' says Paramahamsa. *Brahmacharya* is the most misunderstood concept. It does not imply abstinence from sex. As the very word suggests, *brahma* means 'reality' and *charya* means 'to walk'. In other words, the period of *brahmacharya* is to live with reality; to renounce what we don't have, which is all our fantasies and live happily with what we have, which is reality.

What about married couples? Do they suddenly become unsuitable candidates for the ultimate experience because they are married? Consider the fact that most yoga masters were and are *grihastis* (householders).

Forcing the practice of celibacy (as erroneously understood) upon a person will just result in suppression. Sexual suppression will cultivate fantasies, lust and perversion in a person. The inner pressure so created will be like a volcano waiting to erupt at the slightest provocation.

Celibacy or sexual restraint is not an enforced rule one must adhere to in order to be successful in spiritual life. By practicing yoga we can begin to understand what our body needs and when it needs what. This awareness will ensure that we are never pressurized into either indulgence or suppression.

In regard to married couples, *brahmacharya* never meant full sexual abstinence. *Kama Sutra* is all about understanding and utilizing the power of sexual energy for self-transformation. During the Vedic times, there was an exquisite awareness of our individual energy being an integral part of the cosmic whole. Nothing was done to disturb the harmonious flow and the balance of these energies. The energy was neither poisoned through suppression nor was it dissipated through constant expression.

Paramahamsa declares that *brahmahcharya* practiced in a marriage does not mean celibacy. It implies 'walking with reality'. In other words, it is about dropping the fantasies about how the other person should be. As he time and again says: 'renounce what you don't have; live completely and joyously with what you have.' It is about totally accepting the other person exactly as he or she is. When a person can live with the other totally, with no fantasies, then, something extraordinary happens in the relationship. When we start to accept the other person for whom he or she is, we also start to accept ourselves as we are.

5) Non-possessiveness (*aparigraha*):

Possessiveness is born out of greed to accumulate more and fear of letting go of things or people. As long as we equate our self-worth with our possessions, we make material accumulation a way of life. Fear and greed become an integral part of our day-to-day existence.

Non-possessiveness or *aparigraha* implies that one should practice material simplicity to progress on the path of yoga. People may interpret this as meaning that they must give up their house, car or even family if they want to evolve spiritually.

This is not so, says Paramahamsa. Just enjoy what you have fully and completely. If you do this sincerely, you will be so full with the abundance of Existence that you will not feel the need for more than what is there.

Through our yoga practice, we develop *viveka* or the intelligence to discriminate between what is an absolute necessity and what is unnecessary excess. We are not dependent on external objects to give us happiness; we do not seek security through possessions or people. The obsessive, compulsive need to accumulate more things in order to feel secure just drops away. We become more relaxed; we are able to be in blissful silence with ourselves. With clarity and heightened awareness, we start operating in the higher level of intuition, which guides us unerringly. We learn to let go easily. We become un-clutched.

Niyama

1) Cleanliness (*saucha*):

Through the practice of Nithya Yoga, we realize that cleanliness is both of the body and mind. All aspects of cleanliness at a physical, emotional and psychological level are taken care of.

The practice of *asana, pranayama* and *dhyana* will ensure that we are clean from the inside out and outside in.

Each and every *chakra* relates to some particular emotion. When these *chakra* are cleansed through active meditation, we throw out the emotional grime.

Just like we take our shower everyday to clean our bodies, so too, through meditation we take a 'bliss shower' to cleanse our inner space.

Cleanliness of the body, mind and spirit happens through the practice of yoga.

2) Contentment (*santosha*):

Contentment is a state of being 'enough unto ourselves'. So, external things or persons are no longer needed. Contentment is an acceptance of what we have at any given moment.

Through the practice of yoga, we become filled with peace, silence and energy. It is an automatic process. In a sense, we become so full of ourselves that we drop the continuous habit of seeking attention from others; we stop craving for more and more.

Contentment is a silent expression of our gratitude to Existence for whatever we have.

3) Self-discipline (*tapas*):

Many people understand *tapas* as penance or rigorous practices. *Tapas* means cleanliness, purification. When we do *tapas*, we are creating the conditions for the inner fire to cleanse us. *Tapas* also means the ability to persevere, to be committed to whatever we do.

4) Study of spiritual teaching (*svadhyaya*):

Sva means 'self' and *adhyaya* means 'inquiry'. In other words, means self-study or taking the journey inward. Anything, be it a book, a *svadhyaya* lecture, a seminar, a group discussion, an incident or a situation that helps us to learn more about ourselves is *svadhyaya*.

Traditionally, it meant the study of scriptures or spiritual books. When we do this, a deeper awareness of the self dawns within us and automatically we feel inclined to live in further awareness. Therefore, the desire to study additional spiritual teachings is kindled in us.

5) Surrender to God (*ishwara pranidhana*)

Ishvara pranidhana means that we must do our best in whatever we undertake and leave the consequences to Existence or God. It implies surrender to the Ultimate.

If we stick to the spirit of yoga, we can understand that God is our pure inner self. So 'surrender to God' is nothing but falling in tune with our Higher Self.

Sit and Be Enlightened.

By far, the most beautiful and deep truth of yoga that was revealed by Raghupati yogi to Paramahamsa was that, 'any movement if practiced with a particular idea, belief, awareness or intention *is* yoga'.

During His early days of training with Ragupati yogi, Paramahamsa was taught *asana* to help prepare his body to hold the tremendous energy of enlightenment. Apart from yoga *asana,* Raghupati yogi would instruct Paramahamsa to do other rigorous exercises. Raghupati yogi would instruct him to climb 20 stone pillars that were part of the temple. Paramahamsa could never understand why Raghupati yogi would force him to climb these pillars. He would question Raghupati yogi as to why he was making him do such things. Raghupati yogi would answer, 'For any purpose that you bend or move your body, that purpose and that memory will be completely inserted or recorded into your body and mind. It will become a memory, a *samskara* and will start to express.'

Raghupati yogi meant that the way in which you choose to move your body or the yoga *asanas* which you choose to practice are not too important. The practitioner's awareness and intention while performing the *asanas* is what really matters.

Raghupati yogi would at times tell Paramahamsa to be silent and be peaceful. Then he would immediately instruct him to run around the 25 acre temple with that idea. Paramahamsa used to think this was quite contradictory; the yogi asking him to be in silence, to be peaceful and then getting him to run? However, by the time Paramahamsa had finished running, that idea, that peace would be deeply rooted and recorded in his system.

Paramahamsa says, *'Our body itself is made out of memory. Our muscles store memory. Whether we believe it or not, accept it or not, we are an expression of our own self-hypnosis. Any way you move the body with a faith that this or that will happen in you, simply it will start expressing in you.'* He goes as far as saying, *'Even when you sit, if you observe closely, so many physical movements are happening inside your body. Therefore, ordinary sitting, if you strongly believe that by sitting you will have health, and you sit just for health, simply that health will happen in you.'*

In the West, too much of a disease-*asana* connection has happened; meaning that there is a lot of advice pertaining to which *asanas* we should practice to address certain ailments or disease. In an entire 24 hours, we can see that we do so many movements apart from our 90 minute yoga class. How do we come to the conclusion that only the movements done in our yoga class are can be healing? Paramahamsa always says, 'if you just sit and observe closely, you can see that so many movements are happening in your body. Therefore, even ordinary sitting can be healing. If you sit and strongly believe that you will have health just by sitting, simply that health will happen to you.'

It is not mastery of *asana* or *pranayama* that provides the bliss in the path of yoga, but the

intention with which we do something and the awareness while we are doing something that is responsible for making us experience the state of *nithya ananda*.

Paramahamsa has said many times, 'I am not here to add more movements to your life. I am here to add life to your movements'.

We add life and awareness to all movements and techniques practiced in a 90 minute Nithya Yoga class. We work on strengthening and experiencing our very innate nature which is bliss.

Paramahamsa has said before, 'simply sit and be enlightened'. According to him, we already are enlightened, we just don't know how to express that energy. Nithya Yoga gives us the understanding and the tools to enable us to experience and express that energy. After maintaining a consistent practice, we realize that one *can* simply sit and experience this also. We can sit still and know that we are God!

The Nithya Yoga Practice

Centering Meditation

At the commencement of any Nithya Yoga class, we start with a passive centering meditation. Passive meditation can be described as one that doesn't require physical or active use of our body. Passive meditation is generally a meditation whereby you can rest with yourself. Usually done in a sitting position, with eyes closed, it promotes a very relaxing and calming effect. Passive style of meditation is perfect before bedtime.

Most students, when they come in to do their daily yoga class, will more often than not be rushing in from somewhere else at the last minute. They may have come directly from work, or they may have just dropped their kids somewhere or they may even be coming to class fresh from a conflict they have had with another.

Therefore at the beginning of the class, students are asked to sit comfortably in *sukhasana* (cross-legged on the floor) and simply bring the awareness to the subtle breath entering and exiting the nostrils. Their focus which has been directed outwardly for a large percentage of the day, is immediately turned inward.

Dynamic Meditation Nithya Dhyaan (Life Bliss Meditation)

Why Dynamic Meditation?

Almost all of us carry the impressions of the previous night or the happenings of the day to our yoga class. If they are negative, it is like an energy block in our system. If we don't clear this first in a direct and effective manner, whatever we may do throughout our yoga session will not have the result that should be there. On the other hand, if we walk in brimming with positive energy, the yoga session will help intensify that feeling.

Take a situation like this. If we need to carry sand to our house, we take a container that is big and empty so we would be able to collect sand quickly and with less effort. Similarly, when we clear muck in our inner space, through dynamic meditation, we will benefit enormously from our daily yoga session. We will be able to take in more with less effort and energy. Progress will happen at a faster pace.

With this new approach to the understanding and practice of yoga, a whole new pathway can be created by the mind at the level of brain neurology.

In one of the most stunning studies in the field of cognitive science, neurologist and neuro-psychiatrist Dr Richard Restak has expounded on the plasticity of the human brain. What is this plasticity? It is the brain's inherent capacity to adapt to change. Till recently many neuro-scientists believed that brain plasticity largely ceased by adolescence or by early adult hood at the latest. The common theory was that the brain became fixed in its structure and function. Not anymore.

Genetic mapping, imaging techniques and studies in psychopharmacology have led to an unprecedented understanding of how the brain works and how we can affect its functioning. In the language of yoga, earlier long-standing assumptions have been made to do a headstand!

The physical brain of man a century ago and the one today is very different. Neurologists report that new synaptic connections and neural pathways have formed a new layer called the cerebral layer.

How and why has this happened?

There has been an enormous and dramatic change in human lifestyles in the last century. Like no other time in human history, mankind has been flooded with a bewildering array of stimuli. We have had to cope with the boom in information technology, handling the flood of images through the print and visual media, be victims of violence and mayhem on a day-to-day basis and witness some extraordinary events in our collective history.

These dramatic changes have led to *coping behavior* at the level of neurons and synapses. The scientists concluded that the brain never loses the power to transform itself on the basis of experience. Thoughts, feelings and actions determine the health of our brain. Our belief systems are greatly responsible for the experiencing of well-being. What we hear on a daily basis gets recorded in the brain and an electro-chemical circuit is established.

Training can activate a distinct population of neurons and lead to a gradual strengthening of their connection. In fact just by training, we can bring about changes in key areas of the brain. These changes are evident even a year after the training has stopped. Therefore, engraved memories, samskara, do have physiological support. If the information input is positive, then it transfers itself at the deepest level into a source of empowerment. Otherwise, it can be a source of energy disruption and depletion.

It is very difficult to cut across this cerebral layer and clear the numerous energy blocks through mild means, which is what most traditional practices of yoga are. By beginning the class with a dynamic meditation technique, we open ourselves to a powerful, swift and effective way of clearing all the physical and psychological toxins from our system. It is similar to the effect sweeping a room with a vacuum cleaner as against using a traditional broom.

After the centering meditation, Paramahamsa's revolutionary Nithya Dhyaan (Life Bliss Meditation) is practiced at the commencement of every Nithya Yoga session so students are able to achieve the following;

i) The energy blocks which manifest themselves as toxins at the physical level and emotional grime at the mental are removed,
ii) The dormant nadis (energy channels) are reactivated and revitalized,

iii) An abundance of energy is made available to them, and
iv) Nithya Dhyaan allows students to unclutch from the mind so that one can start moving beyond it. Unclutching from the mind influences the rate at which the physical body can rejuvenate, transform and set itself free from the clutches of physical and mental disease. Samskaras are dissolved and new positive memories can be infused. Thus an entire brand new constitution can be manifested by the individual.

Practicing Nithya Dhyaan is like wiping the slate clean before students begin the asana, pranayama practice. This active meditation generates amazing energy and clarity, helping them to absorb the class at a very deep level.

Nithya Dhyaan Explained

Before we explain what Nithya Dhyaan is, we would first like to give a brief background about how this revelation happened to Paramahamsa. Post enlightenment, Paramahamsa was in silence for an extended amount of time, doing research on meditation techniques, to see how he could reproduce the same experience that happened in him, in others.

The first outcome of his research was the Ananda Spurana Program (Life Bliss Program Level One) where he worked on the seven energy centers (chakra) and devised a meditation technique to energize and cleanse each of the energy centers. This was followed by the Nithyananda Spurana Program (Life Bliss Program Level Two) where he devised meditation techniques for each of the seven bodies to help one have a peaceful and a blissful death. Since then, he has come up with different programs like *Dhyaan Spurana* Program, *Atma Spurana* Program all in an effort to help the individual attain perfection and realize the true self in all possible ways and paths. He came up with around hundred different meditation techniques in all of his programs and each meditation technique was an attempt to raise the individual consciousness by working on some aspect of the Being.

People started asking Paramahamsa if he had one particular meditation technique that he would recommend for everybody and which they can practice daily? When this question was raised again and again, he started pondering over it. Paramahamsa pondered deeply to come up with a technique which is a complete representation of his philosophy, teachings and his experience. He had envisioned a meditation technique, which is holistic and complete by itself and instead of focusing on any particular aspect of the being; it should work on the entire being to transform it and make is ready for the ultimate experience to dawn. And one day, this meditation technique *Nithya Dhyaan* (Life Bliss Meditation) was revealed to him in a flash. In an instant, Paramahamsa could clearly see the different parts of this technique; how each part relates to the other and helps one to raise the individual consciousness. This was all visualized by him in his inner space. We can say that *Nithya Dhyaan* is the pinnacle of Paramahamsa's research in meditation.

This technique consists of five parts. Following, is a detailed description of each part of this meditation.

THE NITHYA YOGA PRACTICE

Part One - CHAOTIC BREATHING:

For the first seven minutes we will sit in *vajrasana* with our eyes closed and our hands on your hips and breathe chaotically. Normally in our body, the energy flows from the *sahasrara chakra* (crown center) to the *muladhara chakra* (root center). We sit in *vajrasana* because this posture helps with the upward movement of energy.

Inhale and exhale deeply and chaotically and completely focus on the breathing. Our entire being should become the breathing. Breath is the best place from where one can start any spiritual practice. There are different kinds of meditation techniques. Some techniques focus

on witnessing, some focus on repeating a word or a *mantra*, however, Paramahamsa suggests that the breath is the best place to begin any spiritual practice.

We have two types of systems in our body. One is voluntary and other is involuntary. The movement of hands and legs is an example of voluntary action. When required, we can move our hands and legs, but we cannot directly control the functioning of our brain, or beating of our heart. Those movements are involuntary movements.

Breathing however, is one system that is voluntary as well as involuntary. Even if we are not aware, the breathing mechanism never fails. We don't stop breathing when we focus our attention on something else, otherwise that would be a calamity. Likewise, we can also control our breathing. The whole science of *Pranayama* emphasizes on control of breath. We can breathe deeply, slowly as and when required. We can hold our breath for long durations or even stop breathing for few minutes. The breath is a link between our voluntary and involuntary systems.

We can never stop breathing and die because then it would be a fight between our survival instinct and our will. Our survival instinct is much stronger than our will. In fact all involuntary movements in our body happen due to the survival instinct. We are living due to our very desire to live. Our very breathing happens due to the desire to live. We might not have observed but our quality of breathing changes depending on your state of mind. Our emotions have an impact on the breathing process. When we are in anxiety our breathing changes, when we are angry our breathing changes and if we are aroused sexually our breathing changes. When we are in love there is a qualitative change in our breathing. Our breathing is directly related to our emotions and it continuously changes as and when the state of the mind changes. When we are in tension the normal advice given is to take a deep breath. The moment we take a deep breath we feel light, more relaxed and the tension releases. Mind and breath are closely inter-related. We can see that when we stop breathing, it becomes very difficult to think. Breath becomes the fuel for the mind. Actually in Sanskrit we use the word *Prana*. *Prana* does not directly mean breath. It means the energy that flows through breath. That energy itself is the life force.

The *pranamaya kosha* or the breath sheath is the where all of our desire memories are stored. Depending on our desires, our *prana*, the breath gets modulated. Our breathing and our desires are tightly coupled. It can be observed that when we have too many desires we breathe very fast and heavily. When we have few desires, we breathe in a more relaxed way. As the breath and the mind are inter-related, changing one automatically changes the other. We have already discussed how our emotions affect the breathing pattern. Likewise, if we were to control our breathing or bring about some change in our breathing pattern it will directly have an impact on our emotions; our state of mind.

All of our memories are stored in our muscles. Paramahamsa strongly believes that if some part of our body is amputated, we would eventually lose the memory related to that part of the body. We can do this small experiment. We can try remembering some past incident in our life without remembering our form. It is impossible. Our form is necessary for us to remember any incident in our life because all of our memories are stored in our form.

We have suppressed many emotions in our being and as a result we are not able to breathe normally. We always breathe shallow. When we breathe shallow, we never release these suppressed emotions and memories that are stored in our muscles. The breathing never touches each and every part of the body. We always breathe in a fixed pattern. Our past *samskaras*, our past memories which are suppressed in our Being create a particular type of breathing pattern in our system. And as a result we attract similar emotions and *samskaras*. Anything within our system has a survival instinct. So anything that is suppressed in our system creates favorable circumstances for it to stay and grow inside our system. If we have suppressed anger in our system, it will keep surfacing itself and create a breathing pattern for its survival. This is a vicious cycle. Our breathing is nothing but a cumulative effect of the past *samskaras*.

Nithya Dhyaan begins with chaotic breathing. We have to breathe as deeply as possible and as chaotically as possible. Our entire being should become the breathing. Understand that the breathing has to be deep. The chaotic breathing should not be shallow. The deep chaotic breathing will start releasing the tension in our muscles and body parts and will start releasing the engraved memories. Normally our muscles are always under stress. Chaotic breathing will loosen the muscles and start clearing the *samskaras*.

Each emotion within us gives rise to a particular breathing pattern. If you observe children, they breathe deeply and blissfully. They don't breathe shallow. But as they grow, they get conditioned by the society, by their pains, pleasures, guilt's, beliefs, stress and other emotions and the quality of the breathing totally changes. Now if we have to shake this pattern; something that has been created due to the emotions suppressed in our system for so many years, we have to insert chaos and we have to create turmoil. Inserting another pattern is not the solution. We have to create utter chaos in our system to dig out all the past impressions. Paramahamsa does not recommend any rhythmic breathing pattern like *pranayama* in this meditation, just chaotic breathing.

This chaotic breathing will destroy all of our past *samskaras*. It is like shaking a tree with dead leaves; all the dead leaves will fall down. Similarly, chaotic breathing is like shaking our suppressed system. All the past engraved memories will be released.

Deep chaotic breathing will also infuse tremendous oxygen and release carbon dioxide from the body. It creates hyperventilation as a result we will feel more vibrant and fresh. Through the increased intake of oxygen in the blood, automatically all the body parts become alive and that creates more bio-energy in the body cells. Normally we always feel ourselves as heavy dead mass and that is because our body is never alive. It is always under stress and tension and something that is tense can never be alive. If the body is made alive with increased flow of oxygen, we will start feeling light, then we will start experiencing ourselves as energy rather than matter. We feel heavy because of the engraved memories.

In fact, in some Buddhist monasteries they use this as a technique to ordain people as monks in the monastery. After you are done with your spiritual disciplines, you are made to walk on grass. If you make a path (grass below your feet dies), then you are not initiated as a monk and more spiritual discipline is prescribed. A person with less *samskaras* will never make a path on the grass when he walks because he always feels light within his system. The burden of engraved memories is less. With increased oxygen and reduced carbon dioxide in chaotic breathing, you will make your suppressed system alive.

The breathing should be so deep, intense and chaotic that our whole being should become the breathing. The bio-energy that is generated will melt our muscles and start clearing the *samskaras* making us feel light, energetic and blissful.

Part Two - INTENSE HUMMING:

put our complete awareness on the humming. We should become the humming.

Humming reduces our inner chatter. Continuously there is talking going on within our minds. We may not be talking to anybody external but internally there is always something that is going on. Humming is an excellent technique to reduce this inner chatter. Normally people find it very difficult to sit without thoughts.

When we suddenly venture into meditation in our middle age, the first thing we would notice is resistance from the mind. Mind will revolt because it does not want to sit silently. When it has been habituated to run for so many years and suddenly it is made to sit silent, obviously it will revolt. In fact people often complain that in an attempt to be thoughtless, they encounter more thoughts. Mind is not accustomed to be silent for so many years and any initial attempt to make it silent is like swimming opposite to the river current; obviously the river is going to protest. This is the time when most people simply give up drop meditation because they become discouraged. They think that meditation is not possible at all for them. However, Paramahamsa says that this is the experience of all the seekers initially. At first we have to make the effort and this very effort is what Paramahamsa defines as *tapas* (austerity). If we feel discouraged by the initial resistance, then we can never succeed.

In the second step, stay seated in *vajrasana*, form *chin mudra* with your fingers and place your hands on your knees. *Chin mudra* is the hand gesture where you touch the tip of the thumb with the tip of the index finger. The other three fingers remain unfolded. The *chin mudra* helps to maintain a balance in the energy flow in the body and keeps the energy within the body by creating a circuit. It prevents the energy from being dissipated out of the body.

In this posture, we should produce a humming sound as intensely as possible, as loudly as possible and as lengthily as possible. We should

There is a mythological story where all the gods and demons are together trying to churn the ocean to extract divine nectar. To their surprise the first thing that comes out after the churning

THE NITHYA YOGA PRACTICE

is deadly poison. Later many other things appeared as a result of the churning and finally the last thing to come was divine nectar. This is a very metaphorical story which has a deep significance in the process of meditation. When the mind is churned in the process of meditation to extract the experience of enlightenment, the first thing to come out is always the negativity that was suppressed in the past. We should not feel discouraged because this is an indication of progress that the negativity is been thrown out. We should continue our effort with the meditation until we experience the supreme state.

In this initial stage when the inner chatter can potentially bother us, intense humming can be an extremely useful tool. It helps us to silence the mind. Our inner chatter is created between the *manipuraka chakra* and the *swadhistana chakra*. This area is also called as *hara*. When we hum intensely, so intensely that we create the vibration of the humming right below our navel, then we stop this process of continuous inner chatter. It is like shaking the *hara*. So the humming should happen from below the navel.

The inner chatter is the sole reason for the mind. Mind is nothing but the inner chatter. And through humming when the inner chatter reduces, automatically we start progressing towards no-mind. We start experiencing a different dimension of our Being.

A good car driver always knows intricate details about his car. Like the noise the car makes at different speeds. If there is any malfunction in the engine and the car noise changes, a good driver immediately senses that and takes corrective action. The passengers won't realize anything but a good car driver certainly will.

Similarly, when we start practicing this meditation regularly, based on the intensity and the quality of our humming, we can start understanding our body functions well. If we over eat certain kinds of foods that do not suit us that well, we will see a difference in the quality of our humming. Automatically, we would adjust our body's needs to make sure that the humming is smooth.

Humming gives us an insight into the subtle vibrations of the body and helps us to take corrective action if necessary. It happens automatically and need not be enforced. Our body and the mind are always out of sync. Paramahasa always tells people that if our body is here then it's almost certain that we are not here. Our mind is always hovering all over the place. Our body has its own innate intelligence which is functioning all the time. It's just that the mind refuses to corroborate with that intelligence. It forces the body into certain actions which later on manifests as disease. Disease means absence of ease. If the body is made to run forcibly, then it is going to revolt some time or the other.

So many times we overeat. The body is giving us the signals that it is full however, the mind is not satisfied. It wants more. And then it goes on filling the body creating more and more damage. The repercussions are then felt later. Creating a harmony between the body and the mind is important for going beyond both. Else we would be caught in this psycho-physical entity and transcendence would be difficult. Humming is one of the best techniques to make a bridge between the body and the mind.

Humming allows us to feel our body as energy. The moment we start humming we start feeling light; as if we are floating. We don't feel the heaviness in the body because humming matches the vibrations of the mind with the vibrations of the body. Body and the mind become harmonious and we start experiencing ourselves as energy.

In this step, we will put our lips together and produce the sound 'Mmmm…' from inside. If we were to put your face inside an empty aluminum vessel and make a humming sound, the sound generated will be similar to this. Note that this is not 'Humm…' or 'Omm…', it is simply keeping your lips together and producing 'Mmmm…' sound.

The humming should be as lengthy as possible between breaths; it should be as deep as possible (from the navel center) and as loud as possible. There is no need to make an effort to take in deep breaths as the body itself will take breaths when needed.

We shouldn't become tense however, just do it in a relaxed manner. We should immerse our whole being and energy into creating this vibration. Try to minimize the gap between the

humming sounds. After some time, we will feel that the humming continues without our effort and that we have become simply a listener. The body and the mind start resonating with the humming vibrations.

After going through the first two steps of chaotic breathing and intense humming, now we move on to the next step where we start entering into the subtler zones of our Being.

Part Three - *CHAKRA* AWARENESS:

In this step we can continue to sit in *vajrasana* or sit crossed-legged if that is more comfortable. In this part of the meditation, we will put our awareness on each *chakra* (energy center) starting from the *muladhara chakra* (root center) to the *sahasrara chakra* (crown center).

We have seven energy centers in our body and we need to understand the meta-physical location of these seven energy centers.

Our personality is made up of three bodies or *shariras*. The physical body (*sthul sharira*), mental body (*sukshma sharira*) and the causal body (*karana sharira*). Similarly there are three states

of consciousness. The waking state, the dream state and deep sleep. Beyond these three bodies and the three states of consciousness lies the true self or *Atman*, whatever you may choose to call. In Sanskrit we call the supreme state as *Sharira Traivalaxana, Panchakosha Teetha, Avastha Trya Sakshi* (Witness of the three bodies, beyond the five sheaths and the witness of the three states of consciousness).

The physical body is the body that we know, which eats, moves etc in the waking state. The mental body is that we use when we dream. We might be lying in our house in the U.S.A however our mind may be in some other country. That time we are employing our mental body. We also use our mental body in the waking state as our faculty of thinking is going on continuously in the waking state. The causal body is that we use when we are in deep restful dreamless sleep. During the entire sleeping cycle there are phases when the mind becomes dormant and there are no thoughts. This is the time when we experience the causal body.

These three bodies are not separate as we may think. They are tightly coupled. Consider two curved lines drawn on a piece of paper in such a way that they intersect at seven different points. If one of the lines represent the physical body, the other line represents the subtle body and the paper represents the causal body, the seven points at which the physical body and the subtle body meet the causal body are the locations of the seven energy centers. These seven energy centers are present at the intersection of the physical, subtle and the causal body. They exist at a metaphysical plane. Some recent research in aura photography has been able to even photograph these energy centers.

These seven energy centers are associated to particular emotions in our Being. These emotions are a result of the engraved memories or *samskaras* which we have accumulated in the past. These *samskaras* block the particular energy center causing physical and mental disturbances. The *samskaras* are present in our being because of the absence of awareness.

When we flood awareness on these energy centers, the energy center starts becoming unblocked from negative emotions and then we start emitting positive emotions like love and compassion. Most of our diseases are psychosomatic. They have their roots in the mind. What we see is just the effect and so we never really understand this mind-body connection. When a particular energy center gets blocked, the part of the body near that energy center gets affected. We can see when we worry too much our stomach gets upset. It is important to keep the energy centers cleansed to promote mental health.

All of these emotions like fantasies, imaginations, fear, worry, attention need, jealousy, ego and discontentment have negative existence. If there is some object in the room and you are asked to take the object out of the room, you can pick up the object and take it out. In this case, the object has positive existence. However, let us say that there is a dark room and you are asked to take the darkness out of room. You cannot really take out the darkness because darkness has negative existence and therefore cannot be taken out. If we turn on a light however, the darkness will be removed automatically. All of these emotions have negative existence just like the darkness in the room and we cannot really take them out. What we have to do is bring in the light of awareness in our being and the negative emotions will disappear automatically.

Once Buddha tied a knot and asked one of his disciples to untie the knot. The disciple tried to pull the knot hard making the knot tighter. Then Buddha asked another disciple to untie the knot. This disciple first looked at the knot carefully. Then he slowly untied the knot. Buddha then explained that if you have to untie the knot of ignorance in your Being, you first have to learn to look carefully. You have to flood your Being with awareness and the negativity will be instantaneously obliterated.

In this step we will put our complete awareness on each energy center starting from the *muladhara chakra* to the *sahasrara chakra*. This way, step by step we move upwards, reaching the crown center. We should become the energy center when we are asked to put awareness on the energy center. We should feel the energy center completely as if our whole being has become that energy center. At the end of this step we will feel energized and light.

Part Four - 'BE UN-CLUTCHED'

Just be un-clutched for the next seven minutes.

The mind is nothing but a collection of thoughts. One thought after the other coming in succession. By our very nature our thoughts are unconnected. They are like bubbles in a fish tank. The bubbles in the fish tank are not connected, they are distinctly separate. But they just appear to be connected. In a similar manner our thoughts are not connected though they appear to be connected.

You can try this small exercise. Sit for ten minutes silently and simply start recording your thoughts. Write down all your thoughts as and when they come. Don't try to control or stop thinking. Just be silent and witness the thoughts coming. The moment a thought comes quickly write it down on paper. Do this for ten minutes. At the end of ten minutes read out whatever is written. You will see that it's a mad man's diary. There is utter chaos. There is no connection between the previous thought and the next thought. All the thoughts are un-clutched and unconnected. Only when you write down your thoughts you come to know that the thoughts have no real connection. You may be thinking about having a cup of coffee and the next moment you may think about some office work, which is pending. There is no real connection between having a cup of tea and the office work. Both are independent events. Even if there are two consecutive thoughts about the same event the thoughts are unconnected as there is no continuity. There is always a gap between these thoughts.

There is a time of silence between the thoughts. The thoughts by their very nature are un-clutched. The problem happens when we connect these thoughts. We connect these unconnected thoughts and suffer. For example; we might have eaten ice cream ten years ago, we might have eaten ice cream seven years ago, we might have eaten ice cream two years ago and we might have eaten ice cream yesterday. All these experiences might have been very pleasurable for us. We might have enjoyed the ice cream each time we ate. The trouble is that we connect these experiences and create an imaginary shaft or an understanding that eating ice cream makes us happy. So we try to repeat this experience in the future. We always connect similar thoughts and create a shaft. It might be our experience that sometimes we don't enjoy the ice cream as much as we enjoyed it some days ago or a year ago. Even if we don't enjoy the ice cream we will make ourselves believe that we like the ice cream. Because we have got into the habit of connecting the thoughts; we unconsciously start accepting that we enjoy ice cream.

Similar is the case with painful experiences. The pain which we experienced ten years ago, the pain which we experienced seven years ago, the pain which we experienced three years ago and the pain which we experienced yesterday are independent events. There is no connection between these events. But we create an imaginary shaft and start thinking that our life is a pain. If we have had many pleasurable experiences in our life we say that our life is a pleasure. But actually neither of it is true. Our life is neither pleasure nor pain because the very process of connecting these events is a mistake. The idea that the thoughts are connected is a misconception. And that too we don't connect all the thoughts. We connect only those thoughts that we remember and create the shaft. Just as from a bunch of flowers we pick up few flowers and create a garland, from millions of thoughts we have, we connect few thoughts that we remember and create a shaft. Creation of the shaft is the original sin.

When we create the shaft we suffer. If we have created a shaft of pleasure then we try to extend the shaft because we want to experience the same pleasure again. If we have created a shaft of pain, we try to break the shaft because we want to avoid the pain. We can neither extend the shaft nor break the shaft because the shaft does not exist. The shaft itself is a myth. The creation of the shaft has become one more shaft for you.

All your experiences are independent experiences. The moment we connect these experiences, we have created hell for ourselves. We have created suffering. Now we can understand why suffering is also imaginary. It is based on something imaginary. It is based on something unreal. It's just an appearance. The shaft is unreal; it does not exist. The suffering that is created due to the shaft is also unreal. Once we realize this we are liberated.

Because our thoughts are so powerful, they have the capacity to clutch with other thoughts and create an imaginary shaft. The process of creating the imaginary shaft is the function of the ego. Ego is nothing separate from the thoughts. Instead it's characteristic of the thoughts to create a shaft. So really speaking the ego does not exist because the shaft does not exist. The shaft is imaginary. Ego is just a name we give to this process of creating a shaft. A sense of continuity is created because of this shaft. This gives us the illusion of the ego.

Right now, all of our thoughts clutch because we think that we have an ego. All of our thoughts by their very nature are independent so the idea of the ego is also imaginary as there cannot be anything connecting these thoughts. So by our very nature we are un-clutched. We are enlightened and just we have to realize it.

Once a disciple goes to a Zen master and asks him 'how can I become Buddha?' The master gives him a tight slap on his face and says that you are already a Buddha. If Buddha comes and asks you that how should he become Buddha what would be your reaction? Same is the reaction of the Zen master. We are un-clutched by our very nature however, this just needs to be understood.

A person based on one's destiny experiences pleasure and pain. We don't have a choice. We cannot choose either pleasure or pain. But we have the choice of not connecting these experiences and creating imaginary shafts. We are attached to a person or a thing because we create shafts. The relationship, which you experienced three years ago, the relationship, which you experienced a year ago and the relationship which you are experiencing now are independent events. The moment we connect these events, we are trying to extend or break the shaft. If the relationship is a pleasurable relationship, we expect the relationship to be pleasurable even in the future. If the relationship is a painful relationship we try to break the relationship or we create an idea that the relationship is not good for us. What we don't realize is that at each instant we are experiencing a new relationship. Because at each instant two new people are associating as by our very nature we are unclutched. The real problem is not caused because of pleasure or pain. The real problem is caused due to our incorrect understanding of both and eventually the creation of imaginary shafts. In the case of a sage, if there is pleasure he will enjoy the

pleasure and forget it. If there is pain, he will suffer the pain and forget it. He does not carry these experiences in horizontal time. The moment we carry an experience in horizontal time we suffer.

We can experience life living in this world and still be centered in peace and harmony. There is no need to renounce anything external. The smaller self has to be renounced. Once we stop creating these shafts, we will realize that the identity, which we were trying to hold on to, was the very reason for suffering.

The moment we drop that identity, we enter into bliss, then the outer incidents won't affect us because we have given up the habit of connecting these incidents. Every incident is a new incident for us and we start seeing life in a much more beautiful way. Everything seems joyful and blissful. We stop taking things for granted.

Once we start accepting life from moment to moment, bliss happens to us naturally. External circumstances can impact us only if you allow them to. Nobody can disturb us without our silent permission. People complain that we may live our life in the moment but if others around don't, they will exploit us. We should be very clear that nobody can exploit us or disturb us without our silent permission. Once we understand that we are un-clutched, bliss naturally follows.

Sankara says in *Nirvanashatkam* '*sada me samatvam na muktir na bandhah, chidananda roopa shivoham*

shivoham', 'I am neither in bondage nor liberated, I am always in the state of equilibrium. I am of the nature of pure auspiciousness, the energy of Shiva.' Both bondage and liberation are concepts created by the mind. Liberation exists as long as there is bondage however, if there is no bondage, liberation will also loose its meaning. That is what Sanakara is referring to. If we are trying to go inward or outward, as long as we are going somewhere we are missing the truth. The very process of traveling or going takes us away from the truth. Truth is here and now and there is no need to go anywhere and no need to travel anywhere. Again, the very process of traveling shows that we have created a shaft. We are seeing some progress. There cannot be any progress, because there is nobody who is progressing. The individual is dying at every instant. Then who will progress?

When we are un-clutched, automatically we will explode in 360°. Then the question of being material or being spiritual won't arise. Sankara says that he is neither in bondage nor liberated. He has gone beyond both and both are just concepts. Our self can never be improved. Some people work on self development. What self will you develop? Is there a self to be developed in the first place? A sequence of un-clutched thoughts is all that we are. If we try to develop the self all you would end up doing is to create a shaft of the idea that my self is developed. It will give you a good feeling. There might be one thought that thinks that the self is developed. But it's merely a feel good feeling. Really speaking the self cannot be developed, the imaginary self can only be eliminated. As

long as we are trying to develop the self, we are creating a shaft.

As long as the mind is present the identification with the unreal continues. Sankara says that '*Brahma satya jagat mithya, jivo brahmaiva na aparah*' which means that 'Brahman is real, the world is unreal and the individual soul is non-different from Brahman.' What he means here is that only when the mind ceases to exist, the Brahman shines forth. The reality shines in its own glory. As long as there is mind, there are thoughts. Thoughts always hover in the past or the future. There can never be a thought about the present. In the present there can only be consciousness. So as long as thoughts are present we will continue to create shafts. We will connect these thoughts and create imaginary shafts of either pleasure or pain. The moment a shaft is created there is identification with the unreal. The reason is that we connect these unconnected thoughts. The very process of connecting thoughts is reason for misery in this *samsara sagara* (world). Because we connect thoughts, the imaginary identity (which Sankara calls as *Jiva*) comes into existence. When the *Jiva* appears the world of *mithya* (made of unreal) appears. When we un-clutch automatically the false identity disappears and the Brahman consciousness is revealed.

We have two types of identities. One is the identity that we show to the outer world and other is the identity that we show to the inner world. The identity that we show to the outer world is called *ahankar*. The identity, which we show to the inner world, is called as *mamakar*.

Both of these identities are in constant conflict with each other. For e.g. outwardly we may project that we are such and such person but inwardly we know that we are lacking in someway or the other. There is always a discrepancy between these two identities. The identity, which we project to the outer world, is always more than what we actually are. A person always tries to prove superior in front of others. Identity, which we project to ourselves, is always less than what we actually are. You might have observed that we are never satisfied with our own selves. Constantly we are trying to improve ourselves in some way or the other. Either we are dissatisfied spiritually or we are dissatisfied materially.

This inner identity that we carry always lacks something and the outer identity that we carry always exceeds the normal. Hence both these identities are always in conflict. That is the reason we have to be very careful when we talk because we rarely talk what we think. If we start directly reproducing our thoughts into words people around us will start running away from us.

Ramakrishna used to say that bringing your thoughts and words together is true spirituality. That will happen when we go beyond these two identities. Both of these identities are false identities. These identities are a result of the shaft we create. They don't exist in reality. As long as we are associating with these identities we are caught up in *samsara*. Once we go beyond these two identities, we become enlightened. All the time we are creating, sustaining and destroying thoughts. The process of creation (*Brahma*), sustenance (*Vishnu*) and destruction (*Mahesh*) is constantly going on. When we stop creating, sustaining and destroying, we go beyond all three and reach the state of *Parabrahman*.

In this part of the meditation, we should carry the understanding with us that our thoughts are unconnected, irrational and un-clutched. There is no horizontal connection between our thoughts. Even if we have thoughts, neither suppress the thoughts nor try to react to them. We should simple watch them with the understanding that they are un-clutched. Automatically, witnessing consciousness will start happening in us. We will go beyond the two identities. You will realize that we are neither the shaft of pleasure nor the shaft of pain but we are the background on which these shafts are drawn.

Understand, that whether we realize it or not, accept it or not we are already enlightened. By our very nature we are un-clutched. We should carry this understanding and sit silently for these next seven minutes and experience the un-clutched state, the state of pure being and bliss. This is the ultimate technique to experience the state of enlightenment.

Part Five - Listen to the Guru Pooja Mantra

In the final step, we just sit silently with a blissful mood and listen to the *mantra* chanting. We should just feel connected to existence and feel the vibrations of the powerful *mantra* within our being.

The *mantra* are a way to express gratitude to existence or the Master for endowing upon us this great wisdom, which liberates us from ignorance and helps us attain the state of eternal bliss, *Nithyananda*.

If you are interested in rituals, you can also perform the *guru pooja* (offering gratitude to the Master) in this step by yourself reciting the mantra and performing the ritual.

If you are not interested in rituals, you can just be silent and listen to the *mantra*. Even by just listening to the *mantra* it would do you immense good. *Mantra* carry vibrations, which can transform your Being to make it more pure and blissful.

THE NITHYA YOGA PRACTICE

Silent Belly Laughter, Intention, Visualization

Silent Belly Laughter

Following *Nithya Dhyaan*, students will remain seated and enter into one of the most important aspects of the class. Technique three contains three elements that make Nithya Yoga unique.

The whole idea of Nithya Yoga is to experience bliss and then to radiate this inherent nature of ours for the other 22.5 hours of our day.

In the West, when people consider the word 'bliss', most conjure up images of 'new age people', people that are unproductive, uncreative and airy. Bliss means the intense excitement which happens in you, without taking anything from the outer world, through touch or seeing or intake or smelling or hearing or by any other method which is hereby mentioned or not mentioned. That is bliss.

In technique three, we firstly work to experience this natural state of bliss. We practice silent belly laughter. Students are asked to simply bring the awareness to the navel region allow bubbling energy to rise up from that center. Students are asked to understand that this energy is their true nature; that their inherent energy *is* 'Nithyananda'. It *is* Eternal Bliss. 'Eternal' means past, present and future. So students understand that they *were* bliss, they *are* bliss and they *will be* bliss.

Intention

Once students have experienced their blissful energy during the practice of silent belly laughter, they are asked to set their strong intention for class. They intend that each movement, each breath will have life. They intend that each movement, each breath will be an complete expression of the Nithyananda state.

Why do we ask students to constantly reinforce the truth that they are bliss?

Thoughts and beliefs have a profound effect on the functioning and well being of our body and mind. So much so, our body is shaped according to our belief system and emotional make up.

Paramahamsa recalls: *'Raghupati yogi would repeatedly tell me that with whatever intention you move your body, bend your body or activate your body, it is that intention, that purpose that will be recorded into your body; those samskaras will start expressing in your body. He meant that the way in which you bend, the method you use to stand up or do yoga asana, all these things are not too important. He said the intention is all that matters. If you have the intention to have good health and do whatever you want for that intention, move your body any which way for that intention, simply health will happen to you.*

This is very difficult for you all to understand because you have invested so much of your time on grooming your body through yoga asana. Instead of transcending body consciousness you have become completely caught up with body awareness. By doing this, the sublime science of yoga has been reduced to the level of a body work-out.'

The truth uttered by Raghupati yogi to Paramhamsa when he was a mere boy so many years ago are being shouted out loud in the corridors of contemporary science!

'We are what our perceptions are; as are our perceptions, so become our actions; as are our actions, so becomes our destiny.' This is not a quote from the *Brihadaranya* Upanishad, but from 'Biology of Belief', a recent work by Dr Bruce Lipton, a celebrated molecular cellular biologist who has presented a groundbreaking theory of how cells behave.

We have all been taught that we behave the way our genes are designed. Dr Lipton disagrees. He postulates that our genes are designed the way we behave!

Our body-mind system constantly transforms itself. Billions of cells are born, live, die and get reborn (a classic parallel to the concept of Brahma (creator), Vishnu (preserver) and Shiva (destroyer). We all are totally new beings every one or two years. Yet we behave in the same unconscious way. We never learn from our mistakes. As Parmahamsa says, 'We are too ignorant to make new mistakes, so we just repeat the same old ones again and again'.

What makes us repeat ourselves and become entangled in our past behavior is the deeply embedded memories, beliefs and values (*samskara*) that we are taught and we cling onto. Though our body is renewed and rejuvenated regularly we do not do the same with our minds. We carry the same mental set up with us in the form of our *samskaras*. These *samskara* lie in our unconscious zone, which holds 90% of our brainpower. It directs us all the way without our being aware that we are being directed. The unconscious brain is far more powerful than our conscious brain. To give an idea, if the conscious brain can process 60 images at a time the unconscious brain can process 60 million images in the same period!

However, we can change. We can change if we become aware of what happens in our unconscious. The agent of change is meditation. Once we become aware of the deep, dark secrets of our unconscious we derive the power to reprogram and rewire ourselves, to transform our cellular structure, to redesign our genes as it were.

Medical science has come up with startling research material that adds further impetus to the fundamental truth that by our very nature we are bliss.

It is interesting to know, that the human body produces several neurotransmitters and neurochemicals, including serotonin, dopamine, and endorphins, which have a specific primary effect of elevating mood and causing feelings of joy and bliss, but none which are designed to primarily lower mood or cause sadness and depression.

Stress hormones like cortisol and adrenaline are designed to help the body cope with adverse events. Originally, in man's evolution, stress was frequent, for example encountering a tiger in the forest. In such cases, the 'fight or flight' reaction was necessary for survival. These hormones provided the flood of additional energy and heightened alertness needed for these situations. However, living in modern society unfortunately causes us to encounter all kinds of stressors on an hourly and daily basis. This is a tremendous drain on the body and mind, and taxes our vitality.

It is seen, that continued exposure to stress results in an uncontrolled self-perpetuating cycle of cortisol increase, which affects the body's well-being by affecting normal serotonin levels. Meditation breaks this cycle and thus elevates mood by increasing endorphins, thereby enabling us to re-connect with our natural stress-free state of bliss.

Recently, in 1992, scientists discovered a neurochemical produced by the body, which attaches to receptor sites in the body that were originally found to be specific for the drug marijuana (*ganja*), a drug which causes feelings of euphoria in the user. This neurochemical was named anandamide by the scientists, after the Sanskrit word for bliss, *ananda*! So, it does appear that the body is designed to express *ananda* and not *dukkha*!

The psychic pain hypothesis of depression proposes that psychic pain, similar to physical pain serves to remind the body and mind that it is causing suffering, and motivates the person to withdraw from the factor causing the pain, and to avoid similar circumstances which could be a threat to health and well-being in the future.

As a wise person once said, 'Pain is inevitable. Suffering is optional'. We thus have the choice of whether to allow the cycle of physical, emotional and psychological stress to continue, thereby increasing susceptibility to physical illness as well as depression, or to break this cycle by yoga and meditation, thereby allowing the body and mind to rediscover its true blissful nature, by allowing the balancing of neurochemicals to happen in a natural manner to its natural state of *ananda*.

What may have been heresy to scientists a decade ago is now the truth that is being slowly accepted, a truth that the Eastern sages and mystics who practiced the inner science knew tens of thousands of years ago and recorded in the scriptures.

Therefore, we are bringing this ancient belief back into practice with the support of scientific findings that bliss is our birthright and whatever we think deeply and continuously has a profound effect on us physically and mentally.

In a Nithya Yoga class, we reinforce a thought, day in and day out, that we are blissful by nature. This practice will impact us at a cellular level. Reconstruction and rewiring of the body-mind system will begin. We will rediscover the truth of who we are. That inner discovery will lead to a totally new perception of ourselves and the world around us.

Visualization

Where visualizing the postures is concerned, the reason we are asked to take a few moments to mentally do the posture rests on sound scientific research. Contrary to popular belief, intelligence is not confined to the brain cells. Each and every cell in the muscle carries the intelligence of the body. Whatever signals are given to it whether conscious or unconscious is stored within.

When we send in a focused suggestion to our body, our body will be ready to do that. In this manner a*sana* and *pranayama,* practice will become easier and more joyful. Instead of pushing our body into a posture, fighting and being violent with it, this visualization allows our body and us to flow harmoniously into the posture. We learn to collaborate and not compete, which again is a fundamental truth in cellular biology. Cells are by their very nature collaborative. They join together to perform a task. They do not understand competition. The thought of competition arises in our minds alone; it is not our basic nature.

It is very clear that if we operate with awareness and clarity at a conscious level, we have the power to reach down to the cellular level and bring about enormous changes. Therefore, our perceptions play a great part in the way we look and behave.

The way in which we perceive ourselves is dependant on the ideas and beliefs we have about ourselves at both a conscious and unconscious level. Through the transformative practice of Nithya Yoga for Being, we are able to bring about a change in the way we see ourselves; we can look forward to enjoying the riches of the material and spiritual world.

If we empower ourselves with this knowledge we can start to realize that every human being is God, waiting to be uncovered. It is just our belief that we are limited in some way that keeps us from realizing the potential of who we are.

Nithya Surya Namaskar

Our body is equipped with innate intelligence to produce energy from the sun. According to the ancient science of *Ayurveda,* the human organism is the ultimate system on planet Earth. It is a living memory bank, a storehouse of the enormous intelligence of all the other bodies on Earth.

Nithya Yoga operates on the belief if plants can produce energy directly from the sun, why can't man? After all, every human being is composed of the same five elements, earth, water, fire, air and ether as the rest of the universe.

The practice of *Nithya Surya Namaskar* will awaken the body intelligence to directly create energy from the sun. For centuries we have suppressed, denied and forgotten the fact that the body has its own intelligence; the wisdom of the ages is stored in each and every cell. The ancient *rishis* understood this truth and therefore declared time and again that we are filled with cosmic consciousness.

Every cell in the body actively responds to environmental stimuli both internal and external. According to Indian tradition, the body is a wonderful mechanism that has the intelligence and capacity to produce energy.

Nithya Surya Namaskar is designed to access the etheric energy all around us. When performed facing the East in the first rays of the morning sun along with the appropriate breathing technique and *Nithya Surya Namaskar Mantra,* the effect on the individual mind, body and spirit is incomparable.

It is said that a daily practice of *Nithya Surya Namaskar* comprising a complete set of twelve repetitions is enough to reap enormous benefits. Nothing else needs to be done.

The *Nithya Surya Namaskar* is so designed that it works on all body parts, every organ, every system, and every *chakra*. It is a moving set of postures done dynamically with the appropriate breathing.

In every Nithya Yoga class, we commence the *asana* series with six to twelve repetitions of *Nithya Surya Namaskar* (Sun salutation). Of all the *asana* practice, the *Nithya Surya Namaskar* is considered the most effective way to limber up, tone, stretch and strengthen the entire body and the spine. *Nithya Surya Namaskar* is regarded as the king of *asana*.

Nithya Surya Namaskar Mantra

A *mantra* is a composition of syllables, words, phrases or sentences that when repeated with awareness has a very powerful and penetrating influence on the mind. In a Nithya Yoga for Being class, before performing each repetition of *Nithya Surya Namaskar*, students chant the corresponding *Nithya Surya Namaskar Mantra*. The *Nithya Surya Namaskar Mantra* are composed of a **bija** (seed) *mantra* and the glorification *mantra*.

The **bija** (seed) *mantra* has no meaning by itself but the vibration of the *mantra* in the human system is very powerful. The 'Theory of Vibration' as expounded by modern scientist seems to be catching up with the truth that was delivered to humanity thousands of years ago by the inner scientists, the Vedic rishis. Scientific studies conducted by Dr Masaro Emoto of Japan has clearly proven that the nature of sound the very quality of vibrations has a profound effect on water. Considering that the human body is more than 80% water, the scientific community is waking up to the enormous possibilities that are available to mankind. On the flip side of the coin we need to wake up to the enormous damage created in the human psyche with words and sounds and the negative qualities attached to them. **Bija** *mantra* do not have any literal meaning, but by chanting them we set up powerful vibrations of energy within the body and the mind. They are six in number and repeated in the following order:

~ om hram

~ om hrim

~ om hroom

~ om hraim

~ om hraum

~ om hraha

12 Glorification *mantra* highlight the various aspects of the Sun. When chanted with complete awareness before every repetition of *Nithya Surya Namaskar*, the *mantra* confer the same qualities on the committed practitioner.

Through this simple though highly effective method, we realize that the outer sun symbolizes the shining intelligence in our inner sky; we come to understand our connectivity to the cosmic energy that is all pervasive.

1 ~ om hram nithya mitraya namaha

salutations to the Eternal Friend of all

2 ~om hrim nithya ravaye namaha

salutations to the Eternal Shining One

3 ~ om hroom nithya suryaya namaha

salutations to the Eternal One who induces activity

4 ~ om hraim nithya bhanave namaha

salutations to the Eternal One who illumines

5 ~ om hraum nithya khagaya namaha

salutations to the Eternal One who moves swiftly

6 ~ om hraha nithya pushne namaha

salutations to the Eternal Giver of strength

7 ~ om hram nithya hiranya garbhaya namaha

salutations to the Eternal golden Cosmic Self

8 ~om hrim nithya mareechaya namaha

salutations to the Eternal Lord of dawn

9 ~ om hroom nithya adityaya namaha

salutations to the Eternal Son of Aditi, the Infinite Cosmic Mother

10 ~ om hraim nithya savitre namaha

salutations to the Eternal Benevolent Mother

11 ~ om hraum nithya arkaya namaha

salutations to the Eternal One who is praiseworthy

12 ~ om hraha nithya bhaskaraya namaha

salutations to the Eternal One who leads to enlightenment

I

II

2

3

Nithya Surya Namaskar Asana Sequence

10

9

4

5

6

7

8

1

Stand with the feet together or slightly apart for balance. Bring hands together into *namaskar* (prayer position) in front of the chest. Keep the eyes open throughout the practice of *Nithya Surya Namaskar*. Chant the corresponding *Nithya Surya Namaskar Mantra*.

2

Inhaling, gracefully sweep the arms up over your head and gently arch the spine backwards.

3

Exhaling, sweep the arms forward and down so the hands touch the floor close to the feet and the forehead comes in close to the knees knees. Please bend the knees to allow for greater ease in doing this.

THE NITHYA YOGA PRACTICE

4

Step the right foot back as far as you can and as you inhale, lift your heart center up.

5

Step the left foot back and come into a plank position with the spine, neck and head in one straight line, your hands placed directly beneath your shoulders.

5a **Beginners Option** Step the left foot back and raise the hips high into the air assuming *parvatasana* (mountain pose).

6

On the exhale, lower the knees, chest and chin to the floor and assume *ashtanga namaskara* (salute with eight parts or points). Keep the chin forward and point the toes.

6a **Beginners Option** On the exhale, lower the knees to the floor, bring your forehead to the floor and stretch your hands in front assuming *shashankasana* (hare pose).

7

On the inhale, gently push with your hands, lift the heart off the floor. Keep the elbows bent at a 90 degree angle and come into *bhujangasana* (cobra's pose).

8

Push with your hands, raise your hips into the air and assume *ardho mukha svanasana* (downward facing dog pose), exhaling. Spread the fingers wide and gently push your heels toward the earth.

9

Gently look forward at your hands and step the right foot forward as far as you can, close to the hands. Inhale, lift your heart.

IO

Step the left foot forward to meet the right hand. Bend your knees a slightly if you need, exhale and bring the head in close to the legs.

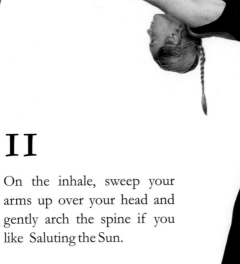

II

On the inhale, sweep your arms up over your head and gently arch the spine if you like Saluting the Sun.

I2

Exhale, bring your arms down and your hands back into prayer position in front of your heart.

VINYASA KRAMA

The intelligent linking of postures that forms a complete sequence in the practice session is called *vinyasa krama*.

The word '*vinyasa*' means 'joining or linking' and '*krama*' means 'the process. '*vinyasa*' is derived from the Sanskrit term '*nyasa*' which means 'to place', and the prefix '*vi*' means 'in a special way'. In other words, it means the succession of activities undertaken with a single focus, which allows a harmonious flow.

Vinyasa krama is the wisdom of the yoga tradition, which states that a practice must be done to suit our life situation. The correct linking of individual *asana* and appropriate breathing in a flowing sequence has a deep physiological impact. Static postures do not lend themselves to expressing the incredible potential inherent in each posture.

In *Vinyasa Krama*, *asana* are performed with a conscious linking of the breath with the movement. If your intention is to practice *asana* to realize the Self, every breath you take will help break down your sense of separation from others.

The *vinyasa* approach is central to the transformative process of yoga. It is a method that can be applied to all aspects of yoga. It is

rooted in the yoga traditions and is yet the most scientific approach to day to day living.

The *vinyasa* method is a step by step process that takes account of the pros and cons of a single *asana*, a situation or an approach. That is why in an *asana* sequence, there are always preparatory postures to get to the main *asana* and counter-poses to relieve any tension. It is important to come back into a position from which we can comfortably resume our everyday activities. For example, it is not enough to want to climb a mountain. It is important that we know how to climb up the mountain, how to stay there and how to climb down. This understanding and preparation is what *vinyasa* is all about.

Vinyasa krama is the art of knowing when you have integrated the work of a certain stage of practice and are ready to move on. It is not just any sequence of *asana* or action. It is one that awakens and sustains consciousness.

Chakra specific *asana*

As we have established previously in this book, the Vedic seers and the modern scientists have proved that seven major centers of boundless energy (*chakra*) exist within us.

The seven chakra

It is a proven fact that these *chakra* correspond to and affect the functioning of specific glands that constitute the body's endocrine system. All of our dis-ease is only caused from an imbalance in any one of these *chakra* because our body and mind are very deeply rooted in our inner consciousness.

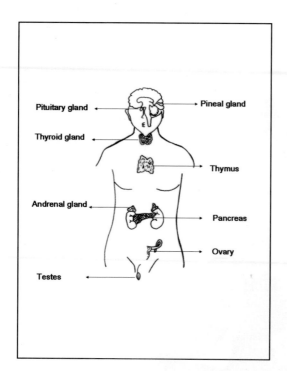

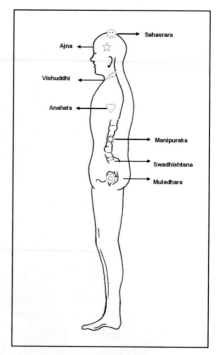

Glands associated with the chakra.   *Location of the chakra.*

The various yogic techniques practiced in a class of Nithya Yoga have been carefully selected so as to ensure that each *chakra* is addressed, cleansed, energized and left generating the boundless energy it has been designed to generate, an energy whose very nature is that of *ananda* or bliss.

In Nithya Yoga, all *asana* are *chakra* specific. At the energy level, the *asana* work on the *chakra* through the glands and at the physiological level, they work directly on the production of these hormones. Along with the other aspects of the Nithya Yoga class, they work powerfully on removing the energy blocks, clearing the mind and detoxifying the system to promote good health and a sense of well being.

PRANAYAMA

In Nithya Yoga, *pranayama* is considered an integral aspect of the whole session. Parmahamsa believes that *ananda* or bliss is the bedrock of our existence. This bliss is available in the very *prana* that is all around and within us.

The word *pranayama* consists of two parts, *prana* (life force energy or simply that which is infinitely anywhere) and *ayama* (to stretch, to extend, to control). In a Yoga class, *pranayama* would mean the various techniques that we use to learn proper breathing to increase vitality, to calm the nervous system and to relax the body-mind for meditation to happen. By the use of various techniques, we enhance the quality and flow of *prana*.

Breath is the link between the body and mind. Whatever happens in the mind is reflected through the breath. For example, when we feel the emotion of anger, our breath becomes short and sharp and blocks the flow of energy from the corresponding *chakra*. When we are an emotionally disturbed state, all we need to do is to take ten deep breaths (inhale and exhale), and watch the emotion coming back to equilibrium. The techniques of *pranayama* are just various methods through which the awareness can be created about the deep connection between our emotions and our breath. The techniques are not important in themselves. What is important is the awareness of our breath when we are in an emotionally disturbed state. Just as the emotions affect the breath, the breath in turn can affect our emotions.

In Nithya Yoga, we go one step deeper.

While using the various techniques of *pranayama* we visualize breathing in bliss and

breathing out bliss. By inhaling the bliss energy and exhaling bliss energy we ensure that while *we* are being energized all that is around us is also benefitted. The message that 'We are bliss' is carried very powerfully and very deeply into our system.

Normally we are used to a practice that tells us to breathe in positive energy and breathe out the negative energy. If we just pause a while and look at what we are doing we will realize that we are contradicting our understanding of our connectivity to the world around us. We are using powerful intentions that are self-defeating.

Two things are happening here: when we say that on each exhale we are breathing out negativity we are unconsciously creating and establishing the *samskara* that *we* are filled with negativity. If we are only going to breathe out negativity, where is the positivity available for the next inhalation? Though Nature has an inbuilt capacity to cleanse the environment of negative energy, it becomes increasingly difficult to do so. If a critical mass of humanity is doing this how long can Nature keep producing healing energies to cleanse this enormous negativity? We must understand that Nature responds to our every thought and emotion. It is our thoughts that create our world.

Nithya Yoga understands and respects this umbilical connection we have with Mother Nature. Therefore in a Nithya Yoga class we learn that at all times we are consciously breathing in and breathing out blissful energy. This sends a subtle and elevating message to the cellular structure: that we and everything around us and we are infused with the blissful, cosmic energy. This further deepens our belief that we belong to a holographic cosmos. We are all One at the level of energy, which is essentially blissful. This truth becomes our *samskara*, the deepest engraved memory.

Paramahamsa declares that breath carries the *prana* like a truck carries goods. Once they enter the body, *prana* and air separate. While air does the physiological work of supplying oxygen, etc, *prana*, life energy, permeates every cell in the body and activates the *samskara* (engraved memories) that are embedded in the system. If the engraved memories are positive and growth promoting, then *prana* will enhance their essence but if they are negative and painful, they get aggravated further.

For those who have attended a class on stress management, a lot of importance is given to exhalation and the lengthening of the exhalation, as it is believed that through exhalation we bring the body to a state of relaxation. This is not so says Paramahamsa, 'inhalation is life and exhalation is death.' The emphasis on exhalation at the level of energy has the same effect as the administering of steroids at the level of the body. At first the effect may seem good and positive, but in the long run, it destroys the system.

Prana is life force and as mentioned earlier, the breath carries the *prana*. The nature of *prana* is such, it activates whatever exists in the system.

Prana does not discriminate between the positive and negative engraved memories. Whatever is present gets energized. So if we are filled with depression, anger, jealousy, low self esteem and so on, the *prana* activates these emotional states.

The mind of the modern man is such that it carries deeply engraved negative memories. Therefore, the transformation through traditional yoga practice is much slower. Nithya Yoga understands the effect of *prana* on *samskaras* (deeply engraved memories). We can utilize the full potential of the *prana* if we cleanse our system before going into the regular yoga practice. In Nithya Yoga, we ensure that every *chakra* is cleansed of these negative emotions through the practice of the dynamic meditations. It is the guaranteed solution to flush out all the energy blocks and toxins within the system. If thereafter we go into the practice of *asana* and *pranayama*, we will very naturally access our full energy potential.

Once the initial cleansing happens, the thought and visualization that 'we are bliss' is introduced and is deepened with every breath that we take. In due course this becomes a powerful memory, the energy of which fills our inner space. This is why it is imperative that a powerful cleansing meditation is done before the practice of any form of *pranayama*.

By focusing on the breath, we bring our mind naturally into the state of *pratyahara* (withdrawal of the senses) and the process of looking inward begins.

When *pranayama* is practiced along with the *asana* and the *mudra*, the numerous energy blocks within our system are removed and the experience of bliss is deepened.

MUDRA

Mudra is the science of finger or hand position that helps to intensify meditation. *Mudra* acts as a catalyst to awaken consciousness. In a very broad sense, Indian classical dancers use mudra to communicate a gesture, a mood or emotion of the inner Being.

The hand and the brain are very intimately connected to one another. In fact, as per science, of all the body parts the hand has the maximum representation in the brain. Whatever is done through the hands has a corresponding effect in the brain. *Mudra* acts as a switchboard of the body and mind. Though primarily therapeutic in purpose, *mudra* confers definite physiological, emotional and spiritual benefits. Like *asana*, it is also a discipline to rejuvenate the body. It actually helps in balancing the five elements (*panchbhutas*) in the human system to their optimal levels

Every individual is composed of five elements or the *panchabhutas*. *Pancha* (five) and *bhutas* (elements) are earth, water, fire, air, space and ether. Each finger represents a particular element. The first five *chakra* correspond to these five elements. By balancing the five elements through *mudra*, we ensure a sense of great well being. Our hands are a complete representation of these elements, as the following diagrams illustrate:

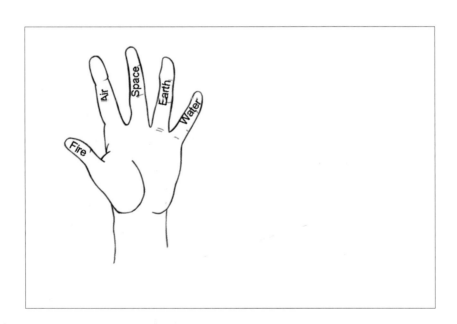

The elements and the corresponding chakras

Apart from representing the elements, the thumb and the index finger hold particular importance. The thumb is symbolic of cosmic (divine) and the index finger (human) is symbolic of consciousness. In other words, the thumb represents God or the higher energy and the index finger represents the individual ego. It is interesting to note that when we are accusing someone of something we always point our index finger to get our point across. Also in very practical terms, if we lose all the four fingers and have the thumb remaining, we can do most of the activity done by our hands. But if our thumb is lost and all other fingers remain, our hands are as good as useless. Symbolically, this establishes the fact that if divine energy is not present in our lives, then our lives are as good as not being lived.

In almost all spiritual traditions, *mudra* plays a big role. In Hatha Yoga, many states of mind are expressed through gestures and body positions. This implies that the reverse is also possible i.e. gestures and body positions can influence the state of the mind.

In Nithya Yoga, specific *mudra* is practiced along with meditations to primarily intensify the meditation. It also works to intensify the energy of the particular *chakra*. By doing various *mudra* we can enhance the energy flow within our system and enjoy a state of great well being.

Additionally, once we learn a *mudra,* we need to harness its benefits in our spare time. *Mudra* should be used judiciously. Never over do them. When we are in tune with our bodies we will know exactly when to come out of a *mudra*.

Mudra can be practiced by itself, time permitting, the minimum being 21 minutes (or one energy cycle-the time it takes energy to travel through all the seven *chakra*) or up to 42 minutes (or two energy cycles.)

THE NITHYA YOGA PRACTICE

SHAVASANA BODY GRATITUDE RELAXATION

Shavasana

Shavasana (translated in English as corpse pose) is traditionally always practiced for at least 5 to 10 minutes at the conclusion of any yogic practice. *Shavasana* is a restorative pose and allows the body to process and understand the information it has received throughout the yoga practice.

It is commonly brushed off by some as being just a rest or a chance to have a short sleep. Truth be told, *shavasana* is essentially the most important aspect of the entire practice. This is where the body receives the class at all levels; physically, mentally, emotionally and spiritually. The body can relax, rejuvenate and heal. If *shavasana* is practiced in totality, it can leave the practitioner energized for hours after their class.

In this modern age, many practitioners rush *shavasana*. Most people find it really hard to lay still for 10 minutes and most lay in *shavasana* and start thinking about where they have to rush to next after class. *Shavasana* should be practiced with the same, if not more, integrity than all other postures.

Your practice is like laying cement foundations. Remember if you step in cement too soon after it is layed, you might ruin the job. The same way, allow your practice to set.

Shavasana is a perfect chance to allow our body to do what it does best; heal itself. We should lay as still as we can for as long as we can and allow the body to relax, renew and rejuvenate itself.

Body Gratitude Relaxation

Our body is a temple, the temple in which our spirit, our Being resides.

We rarely spend any time appreciating and giving gratitude for our body. Most people these days are convinced through conditioning and the media that their body is not good enough. We forget that each of us are unique and have been crafted by God in our own unique way. We should remember that God is an artist. Not an engineer. If God were an engineer, He would have just created one mould, created a production line and manufactured us. Existence has created us all differently. As soon as we start to give gratitude to the body we have been given, we start to radiate a whole new energy. The energy of grace. Grace is not like ordinary beauty. Grace is a whole body language. When one is completely accepting of their body for what it is, they simply radiate this grace and they appear to be the most beautiful people although they might not be physically beautiful.

A true story,

Paramahamsa says, *'All of our skin diseases take root from hatred of our own bodies.'*

A lady with a severe case of psoriasis, a chronic and often incurable skin disease, came to Paramahamsa for healing. While being healed she confided that she had suffered trauma in her childhood that left her with self hatred as well as self guilt. Paramahamsa told her to practice a specific body gratitude meditation for 21 days. The meditation technique involved waking up each morning and touching each and every part of her body with deep love and gratitude. The woman exploded crying: 'How do expect me to love myself the way I am?' Paramahamsa said: 'You have lived in misery for 20 years. Try this just for 21 days.'

In 15 days, the lady was rid of her ailment for ever!

Most of our aches and pains, our skin problems, our hang-ups are just because we don't give our body any attention or appreciation. It is just crying out to be remembered.

In a Nithya Yoga class, we practice *shavasana* at the conclusion. We go one step further by asking the practitioner, while laying in *shavasana* to lovingly remember each and every part of their body with deep awareness and gratitude.

NITHYA AFFIRMATION

Students finally sit cross legged, form *chin mudra* with their fingers and set the intention for their day after class - that every movement, every moment can be Nithya Yoga.

The Nithya Yoga class finishes with Paramahamsa's blessing as the affirmation.

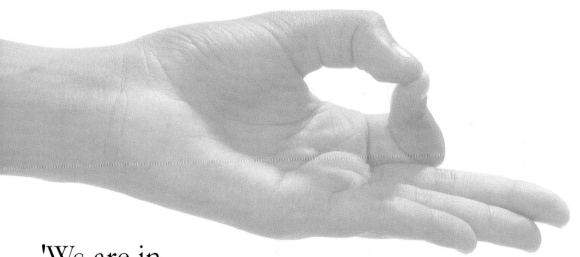

'We are in,
we are one with,
we are radiating and expressing Nithyananda.'

'om nithyanandam'

Finally, students form *atmanjali mudra* with their hands and place the hands in front of the heart center. Students slightly bow their head towards their hands and chant three times the beautiful vibrational mantra 'om nithyanandam' deeply from the navel center.

'om nithyanandam'

May my body radiate bliss
May my mind experience bliss
May my Being express bliss

Nithya Yoga
Practice Sessions

'*I am not here to add more movements to your life.*
I am here to add life to your movements'.

- *Paramahamsa*

Things to know about a Nithya Yoga Class.

What to bring to a Nithya Yoga class

- A yoga mat (preferably of natural fiber like rubber)
- A hand towel or wrist band (if required)
- A bottle of water
- An open mind!

Other important tips

- Do not eat for at least two to three hours before any yoga class.
- Drink a couple of glasses of water one hour before class to ensure the body is hydrated.
- Ensure you drink plenty of water after any yoga class.
- Wear clothes that allow the body to move freely.
- Do not shower immediately after the yoga session. Allow the body temperature to settle.
- Wait for at least 15 minutes before consuming food.

Caution

- If you have a physical injury, disability or recent surgery, pregnancy, heart problems or any other medical condition, please seek professional medical advice before commencement of the Nithya Yoga sessions.
- Anyone with medical problems is advised to do the techniques under the supervision of a qualified Nithya Yogacharya.

'How-to' of the asana practice.

Before practicing *asana*.

Once you become familiar with the series of *asana* (postures) practiced in Nithya Yoga, before performing each *asana,* develop the habit of taking a moment to visualize yourself in the posture.

When you take a moment to mentally perform the posture, you are awakening the body's muscle intelligence. When the body is prepared mentally, when this visualization is practiced, the body will flow harmoniously into the posture. The entire *asana* practice will become a lot easier and much more enjoyable.

While practicing Nithya Yoga *asana*.

While performing the yoga *asana,* as much as possible, try to consciously do the following:

1) Smile softly to yourself. Avoid strain and tension to show on your face. It can change your entire performance and experience of the posture.
2) Keep the eyes soft, wide and always steady.
3) For all balancing postures, always concentrate the gaze on one point in front of you or on the floor. When the eyes are still, the mind will be still and therefore the entire body will be still.
4) Once you are in a posture, do not shift or fidget. If you are uncomfortable, come out of the posture and repeat it with more awareness.
5) Remember while performing the postures, that you are an embodiment of relaxed, blissful energy. With each movement, you are moving the bliss.

Each time you breathe, you are inhaling bliss energy and exhaling bliss energy.

The breath during the *asana*.

The breath is the heart of every posture. Smooth and relaxed breathing will promote a calm mind. The breath will allow you to ease into the posture, maintain the posture and deepen the intensity of the posture.

The breath and the movement must flow in a harmonious togetherness. Generally, unless otherwise specified, all *asana* that open the chest are done on inhale and all others that close the chest are done on exhale.

The quality of the breath must be smooth and easy. It is recommended that as far as possible breathing in *asana* should be done in *Ujjayi pranayama.* Breathing in the movement enhances the effect of the *asana* in the specified area. It also increases awareness and naturally leads to meditation in the practice itself.

Explanation of terms in *Vinyasa Krama* practice.

- '**IN**': Inhale

- '**EX**': Exhale

The 'IN' and 'EX' is always written on the arrow to signify the breathing has to be done in the movement.
- '**T**': Number of times the *asana* has to be repeated
- '**B**': Number of breaths in the postures.

Muladhara
Practice Session

~ Centering Meditation
Duration 2 Minutes

- Sit in a comfortable seated position *sukhasana* (cross-legged on the floor).

- Close your eyes and relax into a soft smile.

- Begin to gather yourself in awareness. This is not a *pranayama* (breath control) technique. Simply observe your normal breathing.

- Avoid concentrating on your breath; just become a watcher. If thoughts arise, allow them to come up. Don't hold on to them, don't go behind or suppress them. Just acknowledge the thoughts and allow them to continue on their way.

~ Nithya Dhyaan (Life Bliss Meditation)
Duration 35 Minutes

Listen to instructions with the *Nithya Dhyaan*
(Life Bliss Meditation) guided meditation CD.

		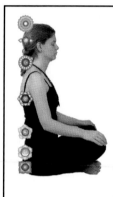		
Chaotic breathing	Intense humming	*Chakra* awareness	Be Un-clutched	*Guru pooja mantra*

~ Silent Belly Laughter
Duration 2 Minutes

- Remain in a comfortable seated position *sukhasana* (cross-legged on the floor).

- Bring the awareness to your belly; your navel center.

- You might like to remember an extremely funny moment in your life; a moment that made you laugh uproariously. A moment that made your belly ache with laughter. Intensely remember this funny occasion.

- Allow that same bubbling energy to rise up from your navel center. This bubbling energy becomes a laughter; a silent laughter.

- Allow the healing energy of laughter to wash over your body. Allow it to touch and penetrate every cell in your system.

- Understand that this blissful energy is your true nature, independent of any event or situation outside of you. Understand that you are *nithya ananda* (Eternal Bliss).

~ Intention
Duration 1 Minute

- Set your strong intention for the class ahead.

- Add awareness and life to each movement practiced.

- Intend that each movement and each breath will be an expression of your true state of *nithya ananda* (eternal bliss). Begin your practice with the understanding that you are an embodiment of blissful energy and each movement and each breath will be practiced with this awareness.

~ Visualization
Duration 1 Minute

Once you are familiar with *Nithya Surya Namaskar*, you can take a minute to visualize your body performing one repetition. This will awaken your muscle intelligence and memory. This visualization will allow your body to flow harmoniously into the posture, as opposed to struggling and fighting to move through the sequence.

~ Nithya Surya Namaskar

- Stand facing the East preferably.
- Chant the corresponding *Nithya Surya Namaskar Mantra* (Pg 89)
- Perform 3 - 6 rounds (6 or 12 repetitions) of *Nithya Surya Namaskar* (Pg 92)

~ Vinyasa Krama for Pachimottanasana

Preparatory Postures

Parivrtta Trikonasana 6T Right/Left Alternating

EX →

← IN

Utkatasana 6T

IN →

← EX

EX →

← IN

Sukhasana Rest
Rest 6 Breaths

Main Posture

Paschimottanasana 6T

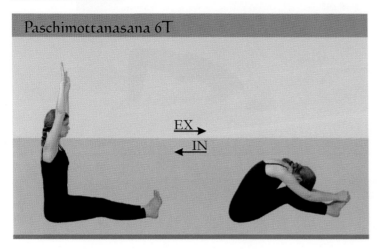

EX →
← IN

Counter Postures

Shavasana Rest 6 B

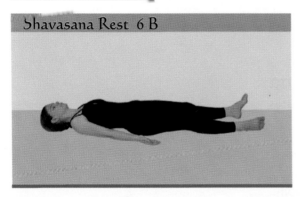

Urdhva Prasrita Padasana 6T

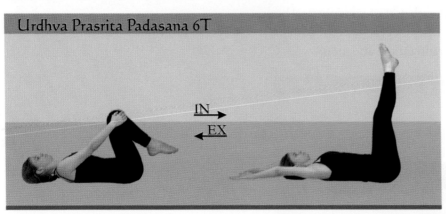

IN →
← EX

Dwipadapeetam 6T

IN →
← EX

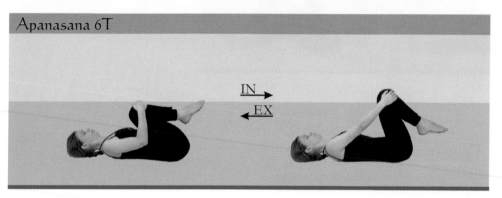

Apanasana 6T

IN →
← EX

~ Body Gratitude Shavasana
Duration 5 - 10 Minutes

- Lie on your back and close your eyes.
- Separate the legs slightly and let the toes fall open to the side.
- Place your arms beside your body with palms facing upwards.
- Let Mother Earth completely support your body.
- Consciously relax each part of your physical body.
- Start to lovingly remember each part of your body one by one. Individually remember each part with deep love, gratitude and affection.

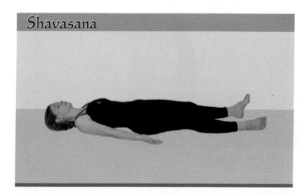

Shavasana

~ Sheetali Pranayama

- Sit in *vajrasana* with your back straight and your eyes preferably closed.
- Roll your tongue to form a hollow as shown in picture (1).
- Start with your chin down. Start to inhale through the hole made by the tongue.
- As you inhale raise your chin (2).
- At the end of the inhalation, fold your tongue backward and close your lips.
- Then exhale through your nostrils as you lower your chin towards your neck (3)
- Repeat for 12 breaths (One inhale and one exhale = 1 breath).
- Relax for a few moments.

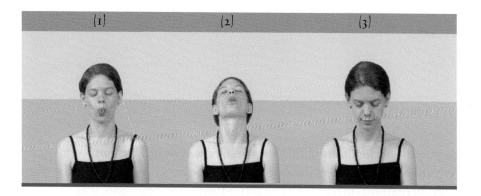

(1)   (2)   (3)

~Prithvi Mudra

Prithvi Mudra

- Place the tips of the thumb and ring finger together.
- Use light pressure.
- Extend the other fingers and place your hands on your knees with the palms facing upwards.
- Focus the mind and direct the breath to the subtle connection between your fingertips.
- This eliminates the energy deficit in this area and activates the root *chakra* in which our elemental force resides.
- The *mudra* acts as a lock, sealing in the energy which you have generated through class.

~Nithya Affirmation

Keeping your eyes closed sit in *sukhasana* (cross-legged on the floor). Form *chin mudra* with your fingers and place your hands on your knees.

Affirm to yourself that:

'I am in, I am one with, I am radiating and expressing Nithyananda'

~ om nithyanandam

Bring your hands into prayer position in front of your chest, bow your head toward your hands. Chant the beautiful vibrational *mantra* three times deeply from the navel center. Allow the truth that you are *nithya ananda* (eternal bliss) in body, in mind and in Being to resonate with you.

'om nithyanandam'

Swadishtana Practice Session

~ Centering Meditation
Duration 2 Minutes

- Sit in a comfortable seated position *sukhasana* (cross-legged on the floor).
- Close your eyes and relax into a soft smile.
- Begin to gather yourself in awareness. This is not a *pranayama* (breath control) technique. Simply observe your normal breathing.
- Avoid concentrating on your breath; just become a watcher. If thoughts arise, allow them to come up. Don't hold on to them, don't go behind or suppress them. Just acknowledge the thoughts and allow them to continue on their way.

~ Nithya Dhyaan (Life Bliss Meditation)
Duration 35 Minutes

Listen to instructions with the *Nithya Dhyaan*
(Life Bliss Meditation) guided meditation CD.

| Chaotic breathing | Intense humming | *Chakra* awareness | Be Un-clutched | *Guru pooja mantra* |

~ Silent Belly Laughter
Duration 2 Minutes

- Remain in a comfortable seated position *sukhasana* (cross-legged on the floor).

- Bring the awareness to your belly; your navel center.

- You might like to remember an extremely funny moment in your life; a moment that made you laugh uproariously. A moment that made your belly ache with laughter. Intensely remember this funny occasion.

- Allow that same bubbling energy to rise up from your navel center. This bubbling energy becomes a laughter; a silent laughter.

- Allow the healing energy of laughter to wash over your body. Allow it to touch and penetrate every cell in your system.

- Understand that this blissful energy is your true nature, independent of any event or situation outside of you. Understand that you are *nithya ananda* (Eternal Bliss).

~ Intention
Duration 1 Minute

- Set your strong intention for the class ahead.

- Add awareness and life to each movement practiced.

- Intend that each movement, each breath will be an expression of your true state of Nithyananda. Begin your practice with the understanding that you are an embodiment of blissful energy and each movement and each breath will be practiced with this awareness.

~ Visualization
Duration 1 Minute

Once you are familiar with *Nithya Surya Namaskar,* you can take a minute to visualize your body performing one repetition. This will awaken your muscle intelligence and memory. This visualization will allow your body to flow harmoniously into the posture, as opposed to struggling and fighting to move through the sequence.

~ Nithya Surya Namaskar

- Stand facing the East preferably.

- Chant the corresponding *Nithya Surya Namaskar Mantra* (Pg 89)

- Perform 3 - 6 rounds (6 or 12 repetitions) of *Nithya Surya Namaskar* (Pg 92)

~ Vinyasa Krama for Shalabasana

Preparatory Postures

Santolasana 6T

IN →
← EX

Makrasana 6B

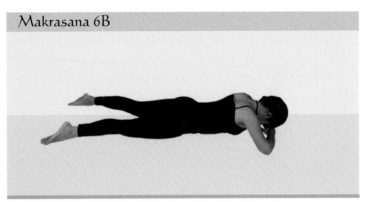

Main Posture

Shalabasana

IN →
← EX

Counter Postures

Ardha Pawanmuktasana 6T Right Leg/ 6T Left Leg

Apanasana 6T

Vinyasa of Vajrasana into Chakra Vakrasana 6T

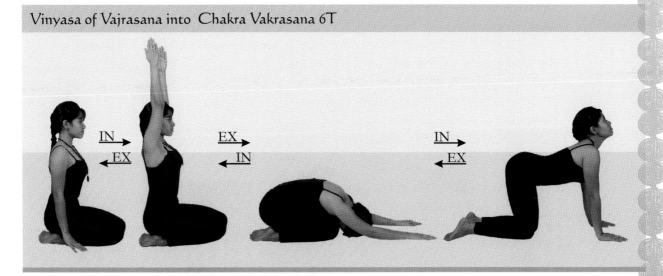

~ Body Gratitude Shavasana

Duration 5 - 10 Minutes

- Lie on your back and close your eyes.
- Separate the legs slightly and let the toes fall open to the side.
- Place your arms beside your body with palms facing upwards.
- Let Mother Earth completely support your body.
- Consciously relax each part of your physical body.
- Start to lovingly remember each part of your body one by one. Individually remember each part with deep love, gratitude and affection.

Shavasana

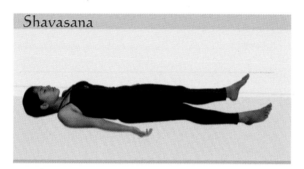

~ Anuloma Viloma Pranayama (Alternate Nostril Breathing)

- Sit in *sukhasana* (cross-legged).
- Fold the fore-finger and middle finger of the right hand (1).
- Place little finger and ring finger on your left nostril and close this nostril off completely. You will begin with an inhale through the right nostril (2).
- Inhale through the right nostril as you slowly lift your chin up (3).
- Now, alternate the pressure by closing the right nostril completely with the thumb.
- Completely exhale through the left nostril as you simultaneously lower the chin back down (4).
- Inhale through the left nostril.
- Exhale through the right nostril.
- This completes one cycle; repeat for 12 cycles.

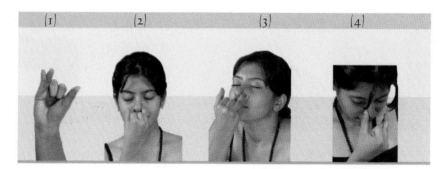

~ Buddhi Mudra

Buddhi Mudra

- Place the tips of the little finger and thumb together.
- Let the other fingers remain extended.
- Focus the mind and direct the breath to this area.
- This mudra helps us regain and maintain equilibrium and balance.

~ Nithya Affirmation

Keeping your eyes closed sit in *sukhasana* (cross-legged on the floor). Form *chin mudra* with your fingers and place your hands on your knees.

Affirm to yourself that:

'I am in, I am one with, I am radiating and expressing Nithyananda'

~ om nithyanandam

Bring your hands into prayer position in front of your chest and bow your head toward your hands. Chant the beautiful vibrational *mantra* three times deeply from the navel center. Allow the truth that you are *nithya ananda* (eternal bliss) in body, in mind and in Being to resonate with you.

'om nithyanandam'

Manipuraka
Practice Session

~ Centering Meditation
Duration 2 Minutes

- Sit in a comfortable seated position *sukhasana* (cross-legged on the floor).

- Close your eyes and relax into a soft smile.

- Begin to gather yourself in awareness. This is not a *pranayama* (breath control) technique. Simply observe your normal breathing.

- Avoid concentrating on your breath; just become a watcher. If thoughts arise, allow them to come up. Don't hold on to them, don't go behind or suppress them. Just acknowledge the thoughts and allow them to continue on their way.

~ Nithya Dhyaan (Life Bliss Meditation)
Duration 35 Minutes

Listen to instructions with the *Nithya Dhyaan*
(Life Bliss Meditation) guided meditation CD.

| Chaotic breathing | Intense humming | *Chakra* awareness | Be Un-clutched | *Guru puja mantra* |

~ Silent Belly Laughter
Duration 2 Minutes

- Remain in a comfortable seated position *sukhasana* (cross-legged on the floor).

- Bring the awareness to your belly; your navel center.

- You might like to remember an extremely funny moment in your life; a moment that made you laugh uproariously. A moment that made your belly ache with laughter. Intensely remember this funny occasion.

- Allow that same bubbling energy to rise up from your navel center. This bubbling energy becomes a laughter; a silent laughter.

- Allow the healing energy of laughter to wash over your body. Allow it to touch and penetrate every cell in your system.

- Understand that this blissful energy is your true nature, independent of any event or situation outside of you. Understand that you are *nithya ananda* (eternal bliss).

~ Intention
Duration 1 Minute

- Set your strong intention for the class ahead.

- Add awareness and life to each movement practiced.

- Intend that each movement, each breath will be an expression of your true state of Nithyananda. Begin your practice with the understanding that you are an embodiment of blissful energy and each movement and each breath will be practiced with this awareness.

~ Visualization
Duration 1 Minute

Once you are familiar with *Nithya Surya Namaskar*, you can take a minute to visualize your body performing one repetition. This will awaken your muscle intelligence and memory. This visualization will allow your body to flow harmoniously into the posture, as opposed to struggling and fighting to move through the sequence.

~ Nithya Surya Namaskar

- Stand facing the East preferably.

- Chant the corresponding *Nithya Surya Namaskar Mantra* (Pg 89)

- Perform 3 - 6 rounds (6 or 12 repetitions) of *Nithya Surya Namaskar* (Pg 92)

~ Vinyasa Krama for Ardha Matsyendrasana

Preparatory Postures

Ardha Chandrasana 6T Right/Left Alternating

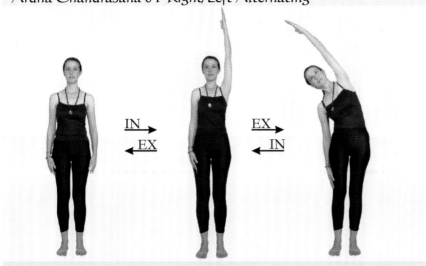

IN →
← EX

EX →
← IN

Parivrtta Trikonasana 6T Right/Left Alternating

EX →
← IN

Uttanasana

IN →
← EX

EX →
← IN

Sukhasana Rest 6B

Main Posture

Ardha Matsyendrasana 6B

EX →
← IN

Counter Postures

Sukhasana Rest 6B

Paschimottanasana 6T

Chakravakrasana 6T

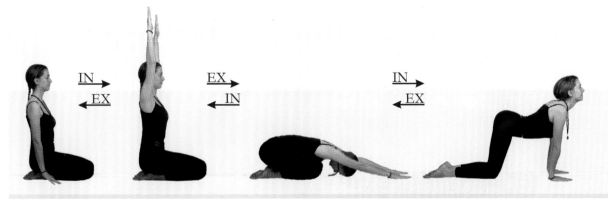

Dynamic Vajrasana 6T

IN →
← EX

EX →
← IN

Sukhasana Rest 6B

~ Body Gratitude Shavasana
Duration 5 - 10 Minutes

- Lie on your back and close your eyes.
- Separate the legs slightly and let the toes fall open to the side.
- Place your arms beside your body with palms facing upwards.
- Let Mother Earth completely support your body.
- Consciously relax each part of your physical body.
- Start to lovingly remember each part of your body one by one. Individually remember each part with deep love, gratitude and affection.

Shavasana

~ Bhastrika Pranayama

- Be seated in a comfortable posture, (preferably *vajrasana*) with your hands on your thighs.
- Very rapidly breathe in and out imitating the bellows. Breathing has to be done rapidly using your abdominal muscles.
- Do 12 breaths (One inhale and one exhale is one breath).
- Relax for a few moments.
- Repeat another 12 breaths (24 breaths in total).

~ Pushan Mudra

Remain seated in *vajrasana*.

Right Hand:
- Place you right hand, palm facing upward on your right thigh.
- Join the tip of the thumb with the ring finger and little finger (1)

Left Hand:
- Place your left hand, palm facing upward on your left thigh.
- Join the tip of the thumb with the ring and the middle finger (2)

Maintain the *mudra* and let your awareness be on the *manipuraka chakra* (3)

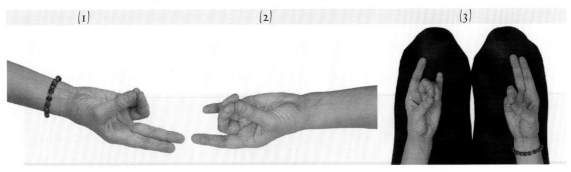

~Nithya Affirmation

Keeping your eyes closed sit in *sukhasana* (cross-legged on the floor). Form *chin mudra* with your fingers and place your hands on your knees.

Affirm to yourself that:

'I am in, I am one with, I am radiating and expressing Nithyananda'

~ om nithyanandam

Bring your hands into prayer position in front of your chest and bow your head toward your hands. Chant the beautiful vibrational *mantra* three times deeply from your navel center. Allow the truth that you are *nithya ananda* (eternal bliss) in body, in mind and in Being to resonate with you.

'om nithyanandam'

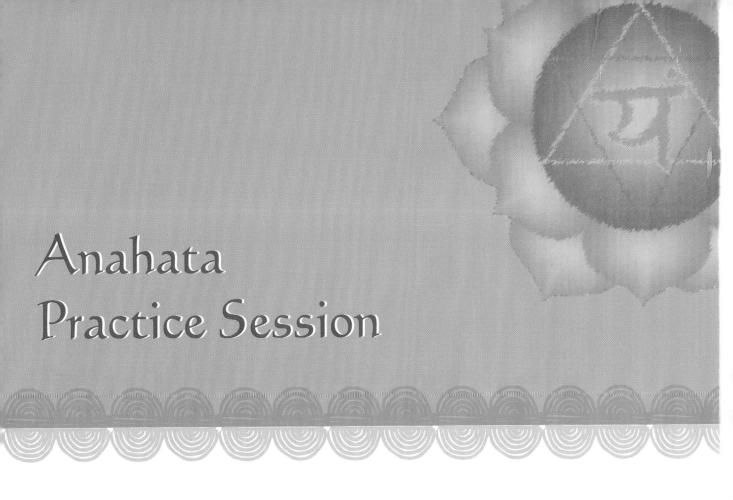

Anahata
Practice Session

~ Centering Meditation
Duration 2 Minutes

- Sit in a comfortable seated position *sukhasana* (cross-legged on the floor).

- Close your eyes and relax into a soft smile.

- Begin to gather yourself in awareness. This is not a *pranayama* (breath control) technique. Simply observe your normal breathing.

- Avoid concentrating on your breath; just become a watcher. If thoughts arise, allow them to come up. Don't hold on to them, don't go behind or suppress them. Just acknowledge the thoughts and allow them to continue on their way.

~ Nithya Dhyaan (Life Bliss Meditation)
Duration 35 Minutes

Listen to instructions with the *Nithya Dhyaan*
(Life Bliss Meditation) guided meditation CD.

| Chaotic breathing | Intense humming | *Chakra* awareness | Be Un-clutched | *Guru puja mantra* |

~ Silent Belly Laughter
Duration 2 Minutes

- Remain in a comfortable seated position *sukhasana* (cross-legged on the floor).

- Bring the awareness to your belly; your navel center.

- You might like to remember an extremely funny moment in your life; a moment that made you laugh uproariously. A moment that made your belly ache with laughter. Intensely remember this funny occasion.

- Allow that same bubbling energy to rise up from your navel center. This bubbling energy becomes a laughter; a silent laughter.

- Allow the healing energy of laughter to wash over your body. Allow it to touch and penetrate every cell in your system.

- Understand that this blissful energy is your true nature, independent of any event or situation outside of you. Understand that you are *nithya ananda* (eternal bliss).

~ Intention
Duration 1 Minute

- Set your strong intention for the class ahead.

- Add awareness and life to each movement practiced.

- Intend that each movement, each breath will be an expression of your true state of Nithyananda. Begin your practice with the understanding that you are an embodiment of blissful energy and each movement and each breath will be practiced with this awareness.

~ Visualization
Duration 1 Minute

Once you are familiar with *Nithya Surya Namaskar*, you can take a minute to visualize your body performing one repetition. This will awaken your muscle intelligence and memory. This visualization will allow your body to flow harmoniously into the posture, as opposed to struggling and fighting to move through the sequence.

~ Nithya Surya Namaskar

- Stand facing the East preferably.

- Chant the corresponding *Nithya Surya Namaskar Mantra* (Pg 89)

- Perform 3 - 6 rounds (6 or 12 repetitions) of *Nithya Surya Namaskar* (Pg 92)

~ Vinyasa Krama for Ustrasana

Preparatory Postures

Chakravakrasana 6T

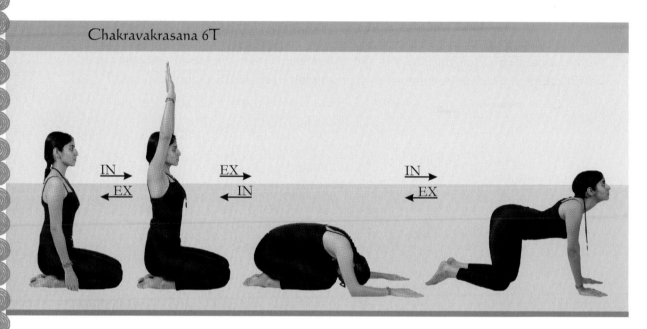

Dwipadapeetam 6T

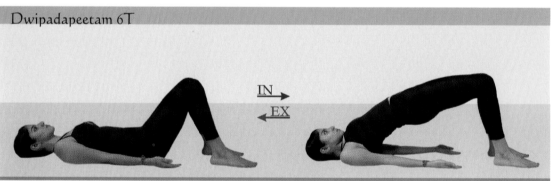

Rest 6 B

Main Posture

Ustrasana

Counter Postures

Shavasana Rest 6B

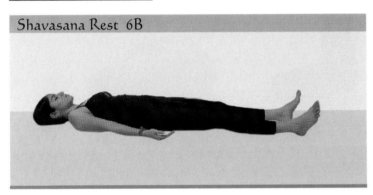

Shavasana with Gentle Arm Raises 6T

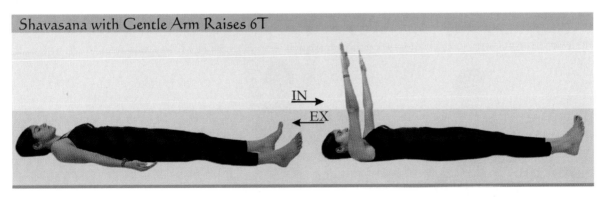

Apanasana 6T

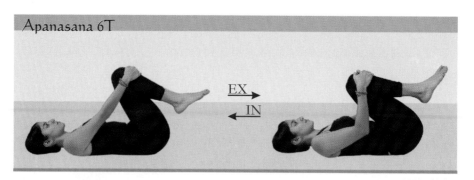

EX →
← IN

Dynamic Vajrasana 6T

IN →
← EX

EX →
← IN

Sukhasana with Gentle Arm Raises 6T

IN →
← EX

Sukhasana Rest 6 Breaths

~ Body Gratitude Shavasana
Duration 5 - 10 Minutes

- Lie on your back and close your eyes.
- Separate the legs slightly and let the toes fall open to the side.
- Place your arms beside your body with palms facing upwards.
- Let Mother Earth completely support your body.
- Consciously relax each part of your physical body.
- Start to lovingly remember each part of your body one by one. Individually remember each part with deep love, gratitude and affection.

Shavasana

~ Complete Yogic Breathing

- Sit in *vajrasana* with your back straight and your eyes preferably closed.
- Inhale and fill the chest first and then in a continuous movement, fill the abdomen.
- On an exhale, slowly draw the abdomen as close to the spine as possible.
- Completely, empty the upper lobes of the lungs in the chest region.
- Before the next inhale, relax the abdomen.
- The breathing should be deep, smooth and slow.

~ Benefits

- Completely stretches the spine and straightens the back.
- Enables the diagram to move freely and naturally.

~ Ganesh Mudra

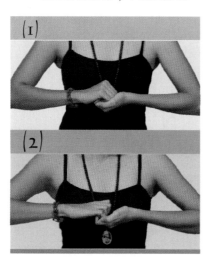

(1)

(2)

- Hold the left hand in front of the chest with the palm facing upward.
- Curl the fingers gently.
- Take the right hand and grasp the left hand (1)
- The back of the right hand faces outward.
- Raise both hands to the level of your heart.
- As you inhale, pull both hands as much as possible without losing the grip (2)
- On the exhale, relax.
- Repeat 6 times.
- Reverse the hand position and follow the same instructions.
- Repeat movement in the reverse position 6 times.
- Let your awareness dwell on the heart area.
- The heart region gets stimulated and strengthened. All the tension is released.

~Nithya Affirmation

Keeping your eyes closed sit in *sukhasana* (cross-legged on the floor). Form *chin mudra* with your fingers and place your hands on your knees.

Affirm to yourself that:

'I am in, I am one with, I am radiating and expressing Nithyananda'

~ om nithyanandam

Bring your hands into prayer position in front of your chest and bow your head toward your hands. Chant the beautiful vibrational *mantra* three times deeply from the navel center. Allow the truth that you are *nithya ananda* (eternal bliss) in body, in mind and in Being resonate with you.

'om nithyanandam'

Vishuddhi Practice Session

~ Centering Meditation
Duration 2 Minutes

- Sit in a comfortable seated position *sukhasana* (cross-legged on the floor).

- Close your eyes and relax into a soft smile.

- Begin to gather yourself in awareness. This is not a *pranayama* (breath control) technique. Simply observe your normal breathing.

- Avoid concentrating on your breath; just become a watcher. If thoughts arise, allow them to come up. Don't hold on to them, don't go behind or suppress them. Just acknowledge the thoughts and allow them to continue on their way.

~ Nithya Dhyaan (Life Bliss Meditation)
Duration 35 Minutes

Listen to instructions with the *Nithya Dhyaan*
(Life Bliss Meditation) guided meditation CD.

| Chaotic breathing | Intense humming | *Chakra* awareness | Be Un-clutched | *Guru puja mantra* |

~ Silent Belly Laughter
Duration 2 Minutes

- Remain in a comfortable seated position *sukhasana* (cross-legged on the floor).

- Bring the awareness to your belly; your navel center.

- You might like to remember an extremely funny moment in your life; a moment that made you laugh uproariously. A moment that made your belly ache with laughter. Intensely remember this funny occasion.

- Allow that same bubbling energy to rise up from your navel center. This bubbling energy becomes a laughter; a silent laughter.

- Allow the healing energy of laughter to wash over your body. Allow it to touch and penetrate every cell in your system.

- Understand that this blissful energy is your true nature, independent of any event or situation outside of you. Understand that you are *nithya ananda* (eternal bliss).

~ Intention
Duration 1 Minute

- Set your strong intention for the class ahead.

- Add awareness and life to each movement practiced.

- Intend that each movement, each breath will be an expression of your true state of Nithyananda. Begin your practice with the understanding that you are an embodiment of blissful energy and each movement and each breath will be practiced with this awareness.

~ Visualization
Duration 1 Minute

Once you are familiar with *Nithya Surya Namaskar*, you can take a minute to visualize your body performing one repetition. This will awaken your muscle intelligence and memory. This visualization will allow your body to flow harmoniously into the posture, as opposed to struggling and fighting to move through the sequence.

~ Nithya Surya Namaskar

- Stand facing the East preferably.
- Chant the corresponding *Nithya Surya Namaskar Mantra* (Pg 89)
- Perform 3 - 6 rounds (6 or 12 repetitions) of *Nithya Surya Namaskar* (Pg 92)

~ Vinyasa Krama for Sarvangasana

Preparatory Postures

Parivrtta Trikonasana 6T Right/Left Alternating

Utkatasana 6T

Dwipadapeetam 6T

Main Posture

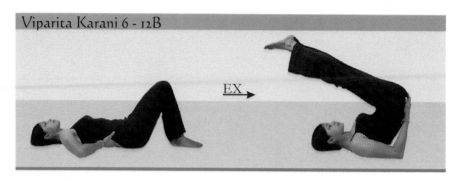

Viparita Karani 6 - 12B

EX →

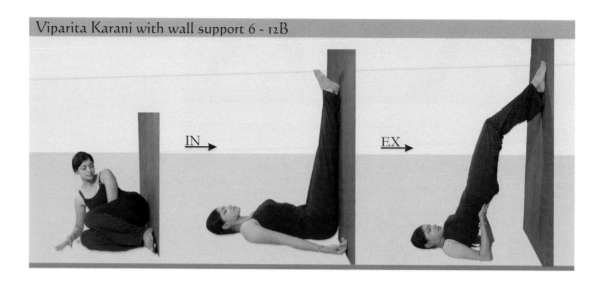

Viparita Karani with wall support 6 - 12B

IN →   EX →

Sarvangasana and Halasana (Intermediate / Advanced Option) 6- 12B

EX →   EX →

Counter Postures

Ardha Pawanmuktasana 6T Right Leg/ 6T Left Leg

EX →
← IN

Shavasana Rest 6B

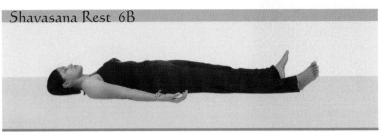

Adho Mukha Svanasana Sequence 6T

IN →
← EX

EX →
← IN

IN →
← EX

EX →
← IN

IN →
← EX

Dynamic Vajrasana 6T

IN →
← EX

EX →
← IN

~ Body Gratitude Shavasana
Duration 5 - 10 Minutes

- Lie on your back and close your eyes.
- Separate the legs slightly and let the toes fall open to the side.
- Place your arms beside your body with palms facing upwards.
- Let Mother Earth completely support your body.
- Consciously relax each part of your physical body.
- Start to lovingly remember each part of your body one by one. Individually remember each part with deep love, gratitude and affection.

Shavasana

~ Ujjayi Pranayama
(throat breathing)

- Sit in *vajrasana* with your back straight and your eyes preferably closed.
- Inhale while constricting your throat.
- Feel a continuous, smooth stream of air passing through the narrowed larynx.
- Exhale and continue constricting your throat to get 'hhhhhh....' sound.
- Repeat for 12 breaths.

~ Shankh Mudra

- Let your hands be in front of you.
- Extend the left thumb and let the other four fingers be together.
- Encircle the left thumb with the four fingers of your right hand (1).
- Now, touch the right thumb to the middle finger of your left hand (2).
- Remember to keep the four fingers of the left hand together.
- Bring your hands towards your throat region (3).
- Keep your awareness on the *vishuddhi chakra*.

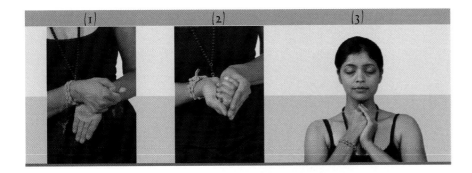

~Nithya Affirmation

Keeping your eyes closed sit in *sukhasana* (cross-legged on the floor). Form *chin mudra* with your fingers and place your hands on your knees.

Affirm to yourself that:

'I am in, I am one with, I am radiating and expressing Nithyananda'

~ om nithyanandam

Bring your hands into prayer position in front of your chest and bow your head toward your hands. Chant the beautiful vibrational *mantra* three times deeply from the navel center. Allow the truth that you are *nithya ananda* (eternal bliss) in body, in mind and in Being to resonate with you.

'om nithyanandam'

Ajna
Practice Session

~ Centering Meditation
Duration 2 Minutes

- Sit in a comfortable seated cross-legged position (*sukhasana*) on the floor.

- Close your eyes and relax into a soft smile.

- Begin to gather yourself in awareness. This is not a *pranayama* (breath control) technique. Simply observe your normal breathing.

- Avoid concentrating on your breath; just become a watcher. If thoughts arise, allow them to come up. Don't hold on to them, don't go behind or suppress them. Just acknowledge the thoughts and allow them to continue on their way.

~ Nithya Dhyaan (Life Bliss Meditation)
Duration 35 Minutes

Listen to the instructions with the *Nithya Dhyaan* (Life Bliss Meditation) guided meditation CD.

| Chaotic breathing | Intense humming | *Chakra* awareness | Be Un-clutched | *Guru puja mantra* |

~ Silent Belly Laughter
Duration 2 Minutes

- Remain in a comfortable seated position *sukhasana* (cross-legged on the floor).

- Bring the awareness to your belly; your navel center.

- You might like to remember an extremely funny moment in your life; a moment that made you laugh uproariously. A moment that made your belly ache with laughter. Intensely remember this funny occasion.

- Allow that same bubbling energy to rise up from your navel center. This bubbling energy becomes a laughter; a silent laughter.

- Allow the healing energy of laughter to implode in your system and wash over your body. Allow it to touch and penetrate every cell in your system.

- Understand that this blissful energy is your true nature, independent of any event or situation outside of you. Understand that you are *nithya ananda* (eternal bliss).

~ Intention
Duration 1 Minute

- Set your strong intention for the class ahead.

- Add awareness and life to each movement practiced.

- Intend that each movement you perform and each breath you breathe will be an expression of your true state of *Nithya Ananda* (Eternal Bliss). Begin your practice with the understanding that you are an embodiment of blissful energy and each movement and each breath will be practiced with this awareness.

~ Visualization
Duration 1 Minute

Once you are familiar with *Nithya Surya Namaskar*, you can take a minute to visualize your body performing one repetition. This will awaken your muscle intelligence and memory. This visualization will allow your body to flow harmoniously into the posture, as opposed to struggling and fighting to move through the sequence.

~ Nithya Surya Namaskar

- Stand facing the East preferably.

- Chant the corresponding *Nithya Surya Namaskar Mantra* (Pg 89)

- Perform 3 - 6 rounds (6 or 12 repetitions) of *Nithya Surya Namaskar* (Pg 92)

~ Vinyasa Krama for Dhanurasana

Preparatory Postures

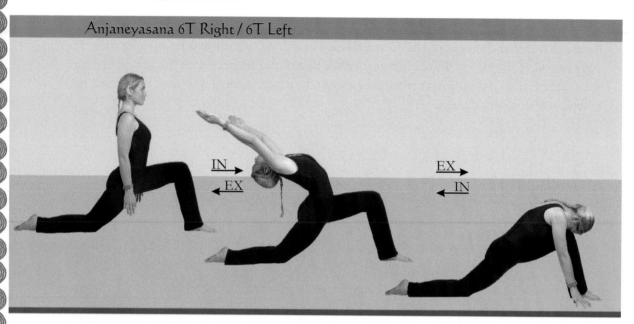

Anjaneyasana 6T Right / 6T Left

IN →
← EX

EX →
← IN

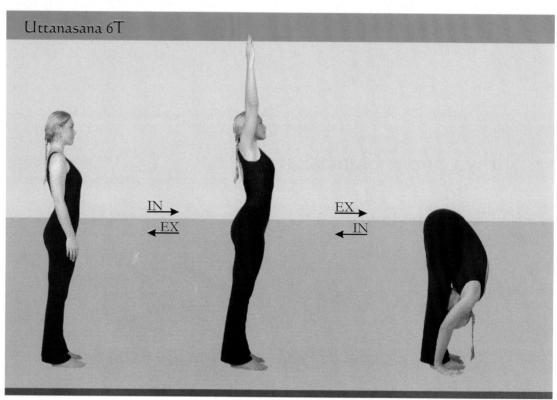

Uttanasana 6T

IN →
← EX

EX →
← IN

Baby Natarajasana 3 - 6 B left Side/Right Side

EX →
← IN

Dwipadapeetam 6T

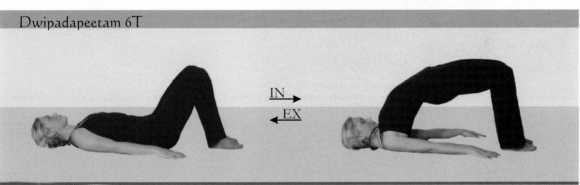

IN →
← EX

Bakasana 6T

EX →

Main Posture

Dhanurasana 6T

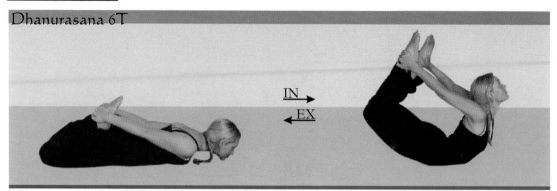

IN →
← EX

Counter Postures

Chakravakrasana 6T

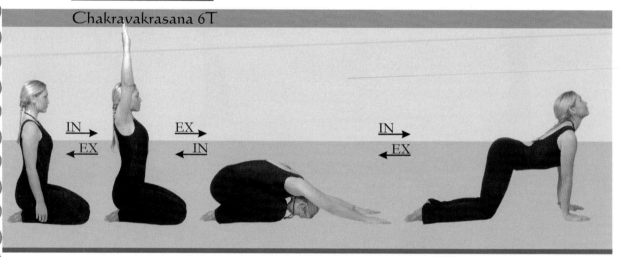

IN →   EX →   IN →
← EX   ← IN   ← EX

Dynamic Vajrasana 6T

IN →   EX →
← EX   ← IN

~ Body Gratitude Shavasana
Duration 5 - 10 Minutes

- Lie on your back and close your eyes.
- Separate the legs slightly and let the toes fall open to the side.
- Place your arms beside your body with palms facing upwards.
- Allow the supportive Mother Earth beneath you to completely support your body.
- Consciously relax each part of your physical body.
- Start to lovingly remember each part of your body one by one. Individually remember each part with deep love, gratitude and affection.

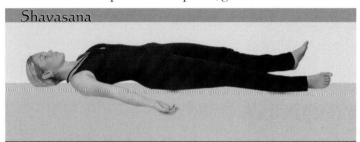

Shavasana

~ Brahmari Pranayama with Shanmukhi Mudra

Sit in *sukhasana* with your back straight and your eyes preferably closed.

Shanmukhi Mudra:

- This *mudra* is a powerful one and disconnects us from sensory information. It helps us turn inward and see who we really are.
- Take both your hands and fix the thumb of each hand in the respective ear cavity.
- Place the first two fingers of each hand over the respective eyelids.
- Place the ring fingers on either side of the nostrils.
- Place the little fingers at the corner of the mouth keeping the lips together.

Brahmari Pranayama:

- Brahmari means the bee. In this pranayama, we exhale by making the humming sound of the bee. When combined with the shanmukhi mudra, it creates tremendous energy to course through the body. A deep sense of ananda or bliss is generated within us.
- Settle into the shanmukhi mudra.
- Inhale deeply through the nose.
- Exhale making the humming sound of the bee.
- Apply gentle pressure with the ring fingers on the nostrils.
- Do not force the exhale. Allow the vibration to resonate through every part of your body.

~ Dhyani Mudra (the empty bowl)

- Place the right hand on your lap with the open palm facing upward.
- Place the open left hand on your right palm with the open palm facing upward.
- Allow the tips of the thumbs of both hands to touch each other forming an empty bowl.
- Take your awareness to the *ajna chakra* (between the eyebrows) and forget all else. Let your breathing be natural and relaxed.
- Through this *mudra*, we signal existence that we are ready to receive everything we need on our spiritual path. This is a powerful technique to sublimate the ego.

~Nithya Affirmation

Keeping your eyes closed sit in *sukhasana* (cross-legged on the floor). Form *chin mudra* with your fingers and place your hands on your knees.

Affirm to yourself that:

'I am in, I am one with, I am radiating and expressing Nithyananda'

~ om nithyanandam

Bring your hands into prayer position in front of your chest and slightly bow your head toward your hands. Chant the beautiful vibrational *mantra* three times deeply from the navel center. Allow the truth that you are *nithya ananda* (eternal bliss) in body, in mind and in Being resonate with you.

'om nithyanandam'

Sahasrara
Practice Session

~ Centering Meditation
Duration 2 Minutes

- Sit in a comfortable seated position *sukhasana* (cross-legged on the floor).
- Close your eyes and relax into a soft smile.
- Begin to gather yourself in awareness. This is not a *pranayama* (breath control) technique. Simply observe your normal breathing.
- Avoid concentrating on your breath; just become a watcher. If thoughts arise, allow them to come up. Don't hold on to them, don't go behind or suppress them. Just acknowledge the thoughts and allow them to continue on their way.

~ Nithya Dhyaan (Life Bliss Meditation)
Duration 35 Minutes

Listen to instructions with the *Nithya Dhyaan*
(Life Bliss Meditation) guided meditation CD.

| Chaotic breathing | Intense humming | *Chakra* awareness | Be Un-clutched | *Guru puja mantra* |

~ Silent Belly Laughter
Duration 2 Minutes

- Remain in a comfortable seated position *sukhasana* (cross-legged on the floor).

- Bring the awareness to your belly; your navel center.

- You might like to remember an extremely funny moment in your life; a moment that made you laugh uproariously. A moment that made your belly ache with laughter. Intensely remember this funny occasion.

- Allow that same bubbling energy to rise up from your navel center. This bubbling energy becomes a laughter; a silent laughter.

- Allow the healing energy of laughter to wash over your body. Allow it to touch and penetrate every cell in your system.

- Understand that this blissful energy is your true nature, independent of any event or situation outside of you. Understand that you are *nithya ananda* (eternal bliss).

~ Intention
Duration 1 Minute

- Set your strong intention for the class ahead.

- Add awareness and life to each movement practiced.

- Intend that each movement you perform and each breath you breathe will be an expression of your true state of *Nithya Ananda* (Eternal Bliss). Begin your practice with the understanding that you are an embodiment of blissful energy and each movement and each breath will be practiced with this awareness.

~ Visualization
Duration 1 Minute

Once you are familiar with *Nithya Surya Namaskar*, you can take a minute to visualize your body performing one repetition. This will awaken your muscle intelligence and memory. This visualization will allow your body to flow harmoniously into the posture, as opposed to struggling and fighting to move through the sequence.

~ Nithya Surya Namaskar

- Stand facing the East preferably.

- Chant the corresponding *Nithya Surya Namaskar Mantra* (Pg 89)

- Perform 3 - 6 rounds (6 or 12 repetitions) of *Nithya Surya Namaskar* (Pg 92)

~ Vinyasa Krama for Dhanurasana

Preparatory Postures

Uttanasana 6T

IN →
← EX

EX →
← IN

Prasarita Padottanasana with side hip opener 6T right / left alternating

EX →
← IN

IN →
↓ EX

← IN

Main Posture

Ardha Sirsasana 6T Back and Forth. Hold finally for 3-6B

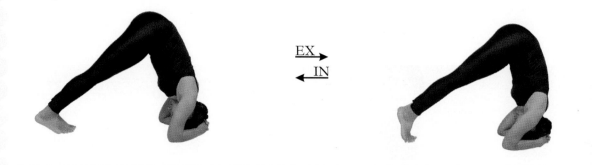

Counter Postures

Variation of Balasana (Childs Pose) 6-12B

Chakra Vakrasana 6T

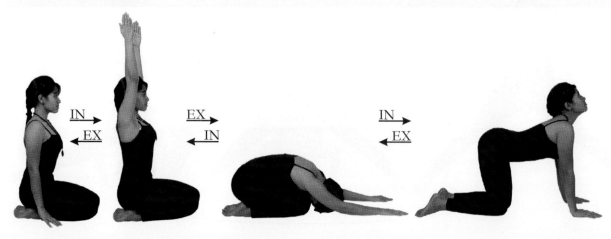

Bhujangasana 6T

IN →
← EX

Makrasana 6B

Apanasana 6T

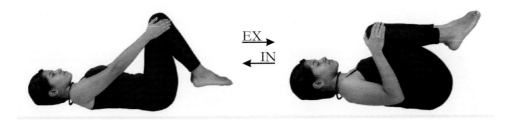

EX →
← IN

~ Body Gratitude Shavasana

Duration 5 - 10 Minutes

- Lie on your back and close your eyes.
- Separate the legs slightly and let the toes fall open to the side.
- Place your arms beside your body with palms facing upwards.
- Let Mother Earth completely support your body.
- Consciously relax each part of your physical body.
- Start to lovingly remember each part of your body one by one. Individually remember each part with deep love, gratitude and affection.

Shavasana

~ Kapalabhati Pranayama

- Sit in *vajrasana* with your back straight and your eyes preferably closed. This is a breathing technique used specifically for cleansing. It has the capacity to remove the heaviness from within our head, clear sinuses and improve oxygen intake.
- Inhale and exhale by deliberate rapid abdominal movements.
- Use only the abdomen and not the chest.
- Keep the breath short, fast and strong.
- Continue for as long as possible, for a maximum of 5 minutes. Relax for a while in a seated position after finishing the *pranayama*

~ Atmanjali Mudra

- Bring your hands together in front of your chest.
- Let there be a little hollow space between the two palms.
- Gently bow your head towards your folded hands.
- This *mudra* when practiced sincerely and regularly creates balance, harmony, clarity, silence and peace. The left and right hemispheres of the brain get activated and coordinated. We experience complete inner serenity.

~ Nithya Affirmation

Keeping your eyes closed sit in *sukhasana* (cross-legged on the floor). Form *chin mudra* with your fingers and place your hands on your knees.

Affirm to yourself that:

'I am in, I am one with, I am radiating and expressing Nithyananda'

~ om nithyanandam

Bring your hands into prayer position in front of your chest and slightly bow your head toward your hands. Chant the beautiful vibrational *mantra* three times deeply from the navel center. Allow the truth that you are *nithya ananda* (eternal bliss) in body, in mind and in Being resonate with you.

'om nithyanandam'

Appendices

~ Vinyasa Krama Instruction Glossary

Adho Mukha Svanasana **Sequence**

- Start by sitting in *vajrasana*.
- **INHALE**, sweep your arms above your head.
- **EXHALE**, sweep your arms forward and place your hands on the floor, with the *ajna* (third eye center) touching the floor if possible.
- **INHALE**, stand up on your hands and knees and lift the heart into cat pose.
- **EXHALE**, curl your toes under and raise your hips up and back into downward facing dog.
- **INHALE**, come forward, lifting the heart into upward facing dog.
- **EXHALE**, again roll back on your toes and lift the hips into downward facing dog.
- **INHALE**, bring the knees onto the floor and lift the heart into cat pose.
- **EXHALE**, return to *namaskar vajrasana,* bringing the hips down to the heels.
- **INHALE**, keep the toes down on the floor sit back up simultaneously sweeping your arms up over your head.
- Repeat this entire sequence for the recommended amount of times.

Anjaneyasana

- Start by standing on your hands and knees (on all fours).
- Bring your left foot forward the foot doesn't have to be directly below the knee.
- Slide the right knee and foot back so there is quite a large distance between the left foot and the right knee on the floor. You should feel a stretch in the hips. Point your right toes.
- Have your arms by your side, look forward and establish your balance.
- **INHALE**, sweep your arms forward and up over your head. More advanced students can actually arch the spine, drop the head back and come into a backward bend.
- **EXHALE**, sweep the arms forward again and down onto the floor, allowing the chin to tuck gently into the chest. Bring your forehead down toward your knee.
- **INHALE**, come back up sweeping the arms up and opening the heart and repeat 5 more times on the right side. Then swap the position of the legs and repeat on the left side for **6** times.

Ardha Bakasana

- From the face down position, bend your left arm and bring your left forearm underneath your chest, with the palm facing down on the floor.
- Lift your chest right up off the ground.
- Press your right hand down on top of your left and lift the chest higher.
- Bend your right leg behind you.
- With your right hand, reach back and take a hold of your right foot. Try to have the grip so that the right hand is palm down on the top of your foot.
- **INHALE**, look forward.
- **EXHALE**, using your right hand and arm strength, start to gently push your right foot down toward the back of your right leg. Keep the chest lifted up.
- Breathe and hold this position for 3-6 breaths. Each exhale, you can encourage your foot down closer the back of the leg.
- On the last exhale, release your foot and allow the right leg to straighten slowly.
- Repeat on the other side.

Ardha Chandrasana

- Stand with your feet slightly apart for balance.
- **INHALE**, sweep your left arm up above your head, really extend and lengthen the spine.
- **EXHALE**, extend and reach up and over to the right side. Bring your right hand down the outside of your right leg and stretch the left arm over. Keep the chin up, both hips forward and the weight in of the body back in the heels slightly.
- **INHALE**, stand back bringing your left arm up over your head again.
- **EXHALE**, slowly allow the left arm to float down by your left side.
- Pause, close your eyes and visualize the posture. See you body moving through the movement blissfully and gracefully.
- Open your eyes and repeat on the left side. Moving right and left is equivalent to one round. Repeat for the recommend amount of rounds.

Ardha Matsyendrasana

- Sit in *vajrasana* (kneeling and sitting on your heels).
- Perform the posture on the right side first. Simply allow the buttocks to fall to the left side.
- Using your hands, help to lift your right leg and place the foot on the outside of the left knee.
- Ensure that both hips are down on the floor as evenly as possible.
- Bring the right hand behind your back (about 1 2 feet away from the spine). Fingertips pointing outward. (Elbow can be bent if needed to create more space between torso and legs).
- Bring the left arm up, and push back the knee with the left elbow. Keep the elbow bent with the palm facing outward.
- Look over your right shoulder.
- **INHALE**, lengthen the spine.
- **EXHALE**, gently twist around, looking gently over your right shoulder more.
- Student can hold *asana* for 6 more breaths.
- After the last **EXHALE**, **INHALE** as you bring the head around to the front.
- Then **EXHALE** and allow the body to unwind slowly.
- Repeat on the other side.

Ardha Pawanmuktasana

- Lift your right leg up and interlace the ten fingers below the knee joint.
- Move the knee out to the right side of the body, so to avoid your ribcage.
- **INHALE**.
- **EXHALE**, pull your right knee down toward your right shoulder.
- **INHALE**, allow the knee to move away from the body. Allow the arms to straighten to their maximum extension without losing the grip with the hands.
- Repeat on the right side **5** more times.
- **EXHALE**, release the right leg down onto the floor.
- Repeat on left side.

Ardha Shalabasana

- Lie down on your stomach with your arms beside you, palms facing upwards.
- Keep the head down with your forehead touching the floor.
- **INHALE**, sweep your right arm up and forward simultaneously lifting your left leg off the floor. Lift your heart and chest from the floor.
- **EXHALE**, slowly bring your body back down to the original starting position with the forehead touching the floor.
- **INHALE**, lift the opposite arm and leg.
- **EXHALE**, come back to the original starting position.
- Repeat right/left alternating **5** more times.

Ardha Sirsasana

- Start by sitting in *vajrasana*.
- Bend forward and place your forearms on the ground.
- Take each elbow with the opposite hand. This will measure the exact distance the elbows should be apart during the half head stand. Once you have this distance, let go of each elbow, release your forearms forward and then interlace your 10 fingers together including the thumbs.
- Bring your head down and place the head just inside the support you have just created with your hands. The crown of the head shouldn't be touching the floor.
- Straighten your legs while lifting the hips high into the air. Start to walk your toes toward your hands.
- Stand right up on your tip-toes.
- **INHALE**, in a very small movement, roll forward on your toes and your whole body will move forward.
- **EXHALE**, just reverse and in a very small movement, move back on your toes. The body will move back.
- Repeat this very small movement **5** more times with your breath.
- After the last exhale, slowly lower your head down into the support formed by your hands. Place the crown of the head on the floor.
- Students should use their arm strength here and not put too much weight in the crown of the head and in the neck.
- Hold this position for 3 6 breaths.
- On the last exhale, slowly lower your knees to the floor.
- Sit the hips back onto the heels.
- Place your forehead on your hands and rest in child's pose for a few breaths.

Apanasana

- Bring both knees in toward the chest.
- Take hold of each knee with each hand (Do not clasp or interlace the fingers).
- **INHALE** in this position.
- **EXHALE**, allow the knees to fall in toward the chest. You don't have to pull the knees with a lot of force.
- **INHALE**, let the knees move away from the chest. Allow the arms to straighten to their maximum extension, however, continue to hold the knees.
- Repeat this movement **5** more times.
- After the last **INHALE**, **EXHALE**, release the grip on the knees and bring the feet onto the floor.

Baby *Natarajasana*

- Stand at the front of your mat.
- Bend your right leg behind you, drop your right hand down and take your right foot from the outside. Bring the two knees close together if possible.
- Focus in front of you. This is a balancing posture therefore try to keep the eyes focused on one point in front to help maintain the balance.
- **INHALE**, stretch the left arm up in front of you bringing the chin close to the shoulder.
- **EXHALE**, start to gently kick your right foot back behind you whilst maintaining the grip with the hand. Keep the right hip down as much as you can.
- Bring the chest down toward the floor a little bit, keeping the heart open, the chin slightly lifted and your gaze steady.
- Hold this position for 3 6 breaths.
- You may feel a stretch on your right quadriceps.
- To release the pose, slowly come back up to an upright position. Bring your left arm down and release your right foot.
- Repeat on the other side.

Balasana **Variation**

- Separate the knees. Keep the toes together.
- Sit down on your heels.
- Bring your forehead down on the floor.
- With your hands, form *namaskar* (prayer position).
- Bend your elbows and bring your hands over the back of your head. Rest the thumbs on the back of the neck.
- Rest here for 6 12 breaths.
- This is a beautiful posture of surrender. Hands in prayer position, have a beautiful attitude of gratitude while maintaining this posture.

Bhujangasana

- Lie down on your stomach.
- Place your hands beneath your shoulders.
- Join the legs together, point the toes and tighten the hips and buttocks.
- Forehead down on the floor.
- **INHALE**, gently pushing the hands into the floor, raise the chest up off the ground.
- **EXHALE**, slowly lower the chest back down and the forehead onto the floor.
- Repeat this movement 5 more times.

Dhanurasana

- Lie face down on the floor.
- Bend both of your knees behind you.
- Start with the right side. Take your right foot with your right hand from the outside.
- Then take your left foot with your left hand from the outside.
- Straighten both of your arms however continue to hold onto the feet.
- Bring your *ajna* center (forehead) down on the ground.
- **INHALE**, start to gently kick your feet back behind you whilst continuing to hold the feet from the outside. Let your shoulders roll back. Lift your heart and open your chest.
- **EXHALE**, slowly lower your thighs, chest and forehead back down the floor.
- Let go of your feet and relax the legs down. Rest your head on your hands and visualize this movement once. See your body lifting up with ease in this more challenging posture.
- Relax into a soft smile and open your eyes.
- Repeat this movement **5** more times.

Dwipadapeetam

- Bring your heels in towards your buttocks and have your feet spaced apart approximately hip width.
- Have the arms beside you with the palms facing up or down.
- If you face the palms upward, hug the shoulder blades in close together and press them to the earth nice and firm.
- Throughout the posture, the back of the head remains on the floor.
- **INHALE**, keeping the shoulders down on the floor, firmly raise the buttocks and hips into the air.
- **EXHALE**, allow the hips to gently lower down to the floor.
- Close your eyes and take a moment to intensely visualize this posture. See your body performing the posture with a lot of ease and grace.
- After visualizing, open your eyes and repeat **5** more times.

Dynamic *Vajrasana*

- Start in *vajrasana*.
- **INHALING**, stand up on your knees, sweeping the arms into the sky.
- **EXHALE**, swim your arms in front of you and around, as you bend forward placing the forehead on the earth. Bring the hands onto the lower back and take the right wrist with the left hand. Or if hands can't reach, simply place the hands on lower back.
- **INHALE**, stand back up on the knees, sweeping the arms into the sky.
- **EXHALE**, sit down on your heels and relax the arms down by your side.
- Repeat for the amount of recommended times.

Makrasana

- Lie down on your stomach.
- Open your legs slightly with your toes pointing directly back.
- Rest your hands on top of each other.
- Place your chin on your hands, so the chin remains forward.
- Close your eyes and relax.
- Feel your connection with the earth.
- Any tension you are holding physically, allow it to drop away.

Parivrtta Trikonasana

- Step the feet wide apart. The further the feet are apart the easier this will be.
- Keep the feet and toes pointing directly forward.
- **INHALE**, raise the arms out to the side, parallel to the floor.
- **EXHALE**, twist to the right and bring your left hand down to your right foot and reach the right hand up to the ceiling. Look up past your right thumb.
- **INHALE**, come back to the beginning position.
- **EXHALE**, twist to the left, bring your right hand down to your left foot and reach the left hand up to the ceiling. Look up past your left thumb.
- **INHALE**, come back up to the beginning position, arms parallel to the floor.
- Repeat this alternating movement **5** more times. 1 time = right and left.

> BEGINNERS NOTES.
> The feet must point forward in this posture.
> If the student cannot touch the foot with opposite hand, instruct them to bend the corresponding knee. You can simplify this posture further by letting the student rest the hand (that is meant to be reaching to the ceiling) onto the lower back.

Paschimottanasana

- Open your eyes.
- Stretch your legs in front of you and bring your heels close together.
- Shuffle your hips back right and left a few times.
- Move your buttocks out of the way with your hands.
- Take each thigh and rotate the inner thigh in and the outer thigh out.
- For most beginners, you should bend the knees up slightly to start, to prevent over rounding of the spine.
- **INHALE**, sweep your arms above your head.
- **EXHALE**, sweep your arms forward, reaching for the toes and bring the forehead down close to the knees.
- **INHALE**, sweep the arms up above your head.
- **EXHALE**, relax your arms down by your side.
- Close your eyes and visualize this movement once. See your body performing the posture with smoothness and grace.
- Open you eyes and repeat *paschimottanasana* **5** more times.
- On the 5th time, keep the head down close to the knees and hold for 3 smooth breaths.

Prasarita Padottanasana with Side Hip Opener

- Spread the legs wide apart and have the toes pointing forward.
- **INHALE**, bring the arms up to your side parallel to the floor.
- **EXHALE**, bend forward and bring the hands down on the floor between your feet. Have the hands about shoulder width apart. Stretch the spine and bring the crown of the head towards the floor between your hands.
- **INHALE**, turn to the right, bend your right knee. Bend your left knee also and place it on the floor. Bring both hands on the inside of your right foot.
- **EXHALE**, bow the head down next to the hands and try to touch the crown of the head to the floor.
- **INHALE**, straighten your legs, stand right back up bringing your arms and hands up parallel to the floor again.
- Repeat entire sequence again, however, next time alternate and go to the left.
- Right and left is **1** time. Repeat this movement **6** times in total.

Santolasana

- Start by standing on all fours (your hands and your knees).
- Lift up into a plank position ensuring your hands are placed directly beneath your shoulders.
- Spine, neck and head should be in a straight line.
- **INHALE**, move forward over your hands, rolling on your toes slightly.
- **EXHALE**, roll back on your toes, into the beginning position. Repeat this movement 6 times.

    NOTE FOR THIS POSTURE:
    For practitioners who find it difficult to remain in this plank position, they can stay on their hands and knees. Simply move back and forth on your hands and knees with the correct breathing.

Sarvangasana and *Halasana*

- Start by lying on your back.
- Bend you knees with feet on the floor.
- Place your hands at your lower back.
- Use momentum and swing your legs up over your head with your knees bent.
- With the knees still bent, walk your shoulder blades closer together and bring the elbows closer together.

- Straighten your legs up into the air. Have the feet flexed or toes slightly pointed.
- Continue to support your back with your hands.
- Look up toward your feet and breathe here for **6 12** B.
- *Halasana* on the final exhale in shoulder stand, keeping your legs straight, lower your feet to the floor behind the back of your head.
- Continue to support your lower back with your hands.
- Breathe here for **6 12** B.
- After the last **INHALE**, exhale and slowly roll your back onto the floor, bending the knees halfway and allow the legs to be on the mat.

Shalabasana

- Lay on your stomach.
- Arms beside you, palms facing upwards, keep the chin forward.
- **INHALE**, sweep your arms forward and up into the air, simultaneously lifting your legs into the air.
- **EXHALE**, bring your arms back down beside you, resting your legs on the floor.
- Just remain in this position on the floor with your eyes closed. Visualize for a few moments, your body doing the posture.
- Open you eyes and repeat *shalabasana* **5** more times.

Shavasana

- Lie down on your back.
- Open the legs slightly.
- Let your toes fall open to the side.
- Have the arms beside your body with the palms facing up.
- Smile softly and relax.
- Try to maintain the stillness required for this posture.
- Scan the body for any tension you are holding and allow any tension to melt.

Shavasana with Gentle Arm Raises

- Start by laying on your back with your feet together and your arms placed by your sides with your palms facing upwards.
- On the **INHALE**, smoothly and gracefully lift your arms into the air.
- **EXHALE**, smoothly let the arms float back down to the floor.
- This movement is very simple, however, remind yourself that Nithya Yoga doesn't rely on the complexity of the posture to receive benefit. Remember to add **LIFE TO THE MOVEMENT**. Add awareness and blissful intention.

Sukhasana

- Sit cross-legged on the floor.
- Place your hands on your knees.
- Close your eyes.
- Just relax for 6 regular breaths.
- Relax into a soft smile and scan the body for any tension you are holding.
- Breathe in blissful energy and breathe out blissful energy.

Sukhasana with Gentle Arm Raises

- Sit in *sukhasana* (cross-legged).
- **INHALE**, sweep your arms up over your head.
- **EXHALE**, gently lower your arms back down.
- Although this seems like a simple movement, add life to this movement. Add awareness and bliss to this movement.

Urdhva Prasrita Padasana

- Bring your legs into the air with the knees bent.
- Have the arms beside you on the ground with the palms facing down.
- **INHALE**, straighten the legs into the air and simultaneously, sweep your arms up over the head onto the floor behind you.

184

- **EXHALE**, bring your arms back down onto the floor and bend your knees.
- Repeat this movement blissfully **5** more times.

> BEGINNERS NOTE:
> If the legs cannot completely straighten, the knees can remain bent. Students should just straighten them as much as possible, within their range of flexibility, without forcing or straining.

Ustrasana

- Stand on your knees with them separated about hip width apart.
- Place your hands on your lower back with the fingers pointing downward.
- **INHALE**, lift your heart and allow your head to gently relax back.
- **EXHALE**, push the hips forward, so the hips are out past your knees.
- If you are a beginning student, you can remain in this position with the hands on the hips, pushing the hips forward, opening the heart and breathing for 6 breaths.
- Intermediate to advanced students can go back and take the heels with the hands. Thumbs on the outside of the heels, fingers inside.
- Continue to push the hips forward from there. At the same time, lifting the heart toward the ceiling. Hold this position for 6 breaths.
- To come out of the posture, place the hands on the lower back, one at a time, and then only, gently roll back up.

Utkatasana

- Stand with your feet separated hip width apart.
- If your hips are tighter, please spread the feet wider and you can slightly turn the toes out to the side.
- **INHALE**, blissfully sweep your arms above your head.
- **EXHALE**, bend the knees and come into a deep squat. Keep the head up and place the hands down on the floor in front of your feet.
- **INHALE**, smile softly and stand up, blissfully sweeping the arms up over the head.
- **EXHALE,** bring your arms down. Close your eyes and visualize this movement intensely.
- Open your eyes and repeat this movement **5** more times.

Uttanasana

- Stand with the feet slightly apart.
- **INHALE**, gracefully sweep your arms up above your head.
- **EXHALE**, pressing your heart and chest forward first, sweep the arms down, folding at your hips. Bend the knees and place the hands on the floor near the feet.
- **INHALE**, lift your chin, lead with the chest, sweep your arms up into the air.
- **EXHALE**, allow the arms to float down by your side.
- Visualize the posture once.
- Open your eyes and repeat *uttanasana* slowly, 5 more times.

Vajrasana

- Start by standing on all fours (your hands and knees).
- Bring your knees and feet together completely.
- **EXHALE**, gently sit your buttocks down on your heels.
- Allow the arms to just relax down beside the body or alternatively you can place your hands on your lap.
- Look forward and focus your eyes on one point in front of you.
- Breathe naturally.

> BEGINNERS NOTES:
> - If you find it difficult to sit directly on the heels, place a blanket or a cushion between your heels and buttocks.
> - You can also place a blanket underneath your feet.

Viparita Karani

- Lie down on your back.
- Bend you knees with feet on the floor.
- Place your hands at your lower back.
- Use momentum and swing your legs up over your head with your knees bent.
- With the knees still bent, walk your shoulder blades closer together and bring the elbows closer together.
- The back can remain at a 45 degree angle.

- Straighten the legs however unlike shoulder stand, you will not straighten them vertically into the air. Straighten the legs so the legs are positioned at an over your torso and head.
- Hold this position for **6-12** breaths.

Viparita Karani with wall support.

- Come close to a wall in the yoga room.
- Sit down next to the wall.
- Put your buttocks close to the wall and swing your legs up the wall.
- Have your arms beside you with the palms facing up.
- Allow your legs to just be up the wall.
- Relax and breathe here for 6 - 12 breaths.
- Eventually, you can place your hands at your hips and while pushing your feet into the wall, raise your buttocks and hips off the floor.

Vinyasa of *Vajrasana* into *Chakravakrasana*

- Sit in *vajrasana*.
- **INHALE**, sweep your arms up over your head.
- **EXHALE**, fold forward at the hips, sweep your arms down, place your hands on the floor and rest your forehead on the floor.
- **INHALE**, come up on all fours, arching your spine and lifting your heart.
- **EXHALE**, bring your hips back down to your heels, resting the forehead on the floor.
- Pressing the tops of the feet into the floor, **INHALE** sit back up, sweeping your arms into the air.
- **EXHALE**, allow your arms to relax down beside you.
- Repeat this sequence for the recommended amount of times.

~ About Paramahamsa Nithyananda

The endless quest of man for the purpose of life ends with this sentence: bliss is the path and the goal. This is the experience and teaching of Paramahamsa Nithyananda, an enlightened master and modern mystic amidst us today.

His mission is to first give the experiential understanding that bliss is not an end goal but the path itself - which is living in bliss 24 hours a day! He brings to understanding that this is possible for every one of us through working in our own inner space. This inner-science research and development, is what is called meditation.

Paramahamsa was born in Tiruvannamalai - a spiritual incubator in South India. A spiritual incubator is a place where the very ambience and energy that is present will cause any meditator to experience his higher potential in multi-dimensions.

Immersed in intense meditation and devotional practices from childhood, Paramahamsa had his first deep spiritual experience at the age of twelve.

Paramahamsa embarked upon a *parivarajaka* (spiritual wandering) at the age of 17 and researched in-depth into spirituality and human wellness. He traveled in India, Nepal and Tibet where the inner science and technology of bliss is still alive for the one who wishes to update his inner software and realize his enlightenment.

It is interesting that from a young age, Paramahamsa studied many spiritual sciences like *bhakti marg* (path of devotion), *yoga marg* (path of union of the body-mind-spirit), *gnana marg* (path of knowledge), *dhyana marg* (path of meditation), *tantra marg* (path of mystical sciences) and other such sciences. He also practiced *karma yoga* (path of selfless service), *raja yoga* (path of penance) and *sannyasa yoga* (path of freedom). He is a living proof of these powerful life sciences.

After years of study and deep meditation, Paramahamsa attained the state of eternal bliss. Today, he is an inspiring personality for millions of people worldwide. He is a living hope for the one who wishes to explore the higher planes of consciousness. From his own experience, he has formulated a Technology of Bliss to explode the individual consciousness, to awaken man to the divinity and bliss within. He founded the Life Bliss Foundation, which has seen rapid growth since its inception. It now spans 33 countries, over 1300 centers and 78 ashrams worldwide.

All his programs are designed for one to fall into the natural space called meditation. He says, 'Meditation is the master key that can bring success in the material world and deep fulfillment in your space within.'

~ About Worldwide Mission

Paramahamsa's worldwide movement for meditation and transformation was established in the year 2003 and now spanning over 1300 centers in 33 countries, it continues to transform humanity through transformation of the individual. It has under its fold, the **International Vedic Hindu University (IVHU)**, Florida, USA.

Nithyananda Meditation Academies (NMAs) worldwide serve as spiritual laboratories where inner growth is profound and outer growth, incidental. These academies are envisioned to be a place and space to explore and explode, through a host of activities, from meditation to science. They offer *quantum spirituality*, where material and spiritual worlds merge and create blissful living; where creative intelligence stems from deep consciousness.

They offer guaranteed life solutions that have seen quick and effective transformation of lives. He has created programs to restore balance to the body, mind and spirit.

A diverse range of meditation programs and social services are offered worldwide through IVHU. Free energy healing through the *Nithya Spiritual Healing system*, free education to youth, encouragement to art and culture, *satsangs* (spiritual gatherings), personality development programs, corporate programs, free medical camps and eye surgeries, free meals at all ashrams worldwide, a one-year residential spiritual training program in India, an in-house *gurukul* system of learning for children and many more such services are offered around the world.

Ananda Sevaks of the **Nithya Dheera Seva Sena (NDSS)** volunteer force - comprising growing numbers of dedicated volunteers around the world support the mission with great enthusiasm.

~ Offerings from the Nithyananda Yoga Foundation

- Nithya Yoga for Kids

Paramahamsa says,

'Every child is a flower waiting to bloom and radiate its unique beauty and fragrance. Children are born in the blissful state of yoga. Facilitating this natural expression is the sole purpose of Nithya Yoga. Children are encouraged to express their inherent knowledge, intelligence, creativity, love and bliss.'

Nithya Yoga for Kids is a fun 20 minute session that is taught to children in Paramahamsa's ashrams worldwide independently and as part of a 1 day program that is offered for kids called 'Little Anandas'.

It helps your child to be balanced physically, mentally and emotionally. This is the greatest gift you as a parent can offer your child.

Please see pg ( ) for a list of teachers worldwide who offer Nithya Yoga for Kids.

- Nithya Yoga Travel Study Progam 'In the Footsteps of Patanjali'

In the Footsteps of Patanjali is a 15 day pilgrimage throughout the culturally rich state of Tamil Nadu in Southern India. The tour covers over 15 different towns/cities, most of which are said to have spiritual significance in the life of Patanjali (The Father of Yoga); including Chidambaram (Patanjali's birthplace) and Rameshwaram (where Patanjali attained Samadhi).

This yoga pilgrimage is a veritable feast for the body, mind and soul. You will experience the grandeur of the awesome temples, the cultural diversity and the colorful traditions of the local people. It is a wonderful chance to experience the truth and the essence of Nithya Yoga as a way of life.

- Nithya Yoga - International Vedic Hindu University Online 3 credit course

The International Vedic Hindu University* offers a range of online courses aimed at providing students an in-depth study on the various areas of Vedic science. Nithya Yoga, is one such Vedic science. Although recently introduced to the world, Nithya Yoga is in fact the most ancient system of yoga as originally presented by Patanjali. Patanjali's yoga and his *yoga sutra* were intended to give us an understanding of the mind; the mind which is the considered the greatest obstacle in our path of experiencing yoga (enlightenment).

In the Nithya Yoga online course, a student will;

- Understand the pure essence of yoga as it was presented during the Eastern Vedic period in contrast with how it presented today in the West.
- Be provided with a background into the life of Patanjali (The Founder of the Yoga System).
- Gain an insight into the teachings of Patanjali *Ashtanga Yoga* System and the *Yoga Sutra*.
- Learn how the 'MIND' is the major obstacle in achieving the state of yoga.
- Learn of Paramahamas's technique to go beyond the mind - 'Being Un-clutched.'
- Be introduced to the concepts of Nithya Yoga.
- Learn how most of the Nithya Yoga concepts are the original message and intention of Patanjali.
- Study how science is proving that our mind creates our body. Students will study a couple of recent studies that have been conducted to prove that thoughts and ideas can influence and create our body. These studies include Dr Bruce Lipton and Dr Masuro Emoto.
- Learn about the power of visualization and body intelligence.
- Learn about the 7 major energy centers (*chakras*) existing within the human make-up and how they influence our overall well-being and energy.
- Learn about dynamic meditation and why it is an essential practice when addressing the contemporary mind. Students will understand the elements of one particular dynamic meditation called Nithya Dhyaan (Life Bliss Meditation).

- Gain a thorough understanding of different yogic practices including; *Nithya Surya Namaskar, Vinyasa Krama, Pranayama, Mudra* and relaxation.
- Finally put into practice the concepts learnt and experience all of the yogic techniques beautifully blended into one Nithya Yoga session.

* Hindu University of America

- Nithya Yoga Teachers Training

Is yoga and sharing it with others in its true essence and as Patanjali originally intended your true passion?

Are you ready to teach a system of yoga that is from the very roots of Vedic science?

Have you come to a point in your regular *asana* practice where you are wondering, 'I think there are deeper meanings and more to experience from this thing we call 'yoga'?

Are you ready to gain the understanding and experience for yourself that every moment in your life can become yoga. Are you ready to experience yoga as an entire lifestyle?

Do you want to experience *not* adding more movements to your life, rather, adding more *life* to your movements?

If you have answered yes to one or all of these, Nithya Yoga Teachers Training is for you.
This training is not just any yoga teachers training; it is a complete inner transformation for the participant.

It is a chance to live yoga for 12-15 days.

It is a chance to learn not only the portable knowledge (knowledge we receive from books etc), however, also to have the non-portable experience which is the ultimate because it is the knowledge gained through psychological revolution regarding the Self.

It is the ultimate irreversible alchemy.

~ Contact us:

USA:

Nithyananda Yoga Foundation
928 Huntington Drive,
Duarte, Los Angeles
CA 91010
USA
Ph: 626 205 3286
Email: enquiries@nithyayoga.org
URL: www.nithyayoga.org

INDIA:

Nithyananda Dhyanapeetam
Nithyanandapuri
Kallugopahalli
Mysore Road, Bidadi
Bangalore - 562 109
Karnataka
INDIA
Ph.: 91 +80 65591844 / 27202084
Fax: 91 +80 27202084
Email: mail@dhyanapeetam.org
URL: www.dhyanapeetam.org

For other ashrams and centers worldwide, visit www.nithyananda.org

~ Suggested for further reading

Paramahamsa's Foundation offers many volumes of books and CDs across 21 languages. They carry the powerful words of the Master as tools of blissful living, for any type of person. A few of the books are listed here:

Nithya Yoga for Kids
Guaranteed Solutions for sex, fear, worry etc.
Nithyananda Vol. 1 (The first volume of a biographical account of Paramahamsa)
Meditation is for you
Bliss is the path and the goal
The only way out is IN
Rising in love with the Master
Uncommon answers to common questions
Open the door…Let the breeze in!

To purchase books and other items, visit www.lifeblissgalleria.com or contact us.

~Nithya Yogacharyas around the world:

CANADA

Sri Nithyananda Nesan (Mel Diamond)
Vancouver, British Columbia, Canada
meldiamond@whooshnet.com

Ma Nithya Hridyananda (Sheila Gouchie)
Vancouver, British Columbia, Canada
sheilazoap@hotmail.com

Ma Nithya Geetapriyananda (Joanna Szczecka)
Vancouver, British Columbia, Canada
joannasa@telusnet.com

BRAZIL

Ma Nithyananda Digambara
Rio de Janeiro, Brazil
anandadigambara@gmail.com

Ma Nithya Varshanananda
Rio de Janeiro, Brazil
m.michahelles@gmail.com

FRENCH WEST INDIES

Ma Nithyananda Nivritti
Guadeloupe, French West Indies
nithyananda-nivritti@yahoo.com

INDIA

Ma Nithya Maneeshananda
Bangalore, Karnartaka, India.
nithya.maneesha@gmail.com

Ma Nithyananda Gnaneshwari Mayi
Bidadi Ashram, Bangalore, Karnataka, India
gnaneshwari.mayi@gmail.com

Ma Nithyananda Sanjayi (Shruti Rao)
Salem, Tamil Nadu, India
nithyananda.sanjayi@gmail.com

Ma Nithyananda Ranjani (Sharlene Das)
Bangalore, Karnataka, India
sharlene.das@gmail.com

Ma Nithya Chandrananda
Bidadi Ashram, Bangalore, Karnataka, India
nithyachandrananda@yahoo.fr

Ma Nithya Achalananda
Bidadi Ashram, Bangalore, Karnataka, India
nithya.achalananda@gmail.com

Ma Nithyananda Joshtri (Yeshodhara Sinh)
Delhi, Andra Pradesh, India
nithyananda.joshtri@gmail.com

Ma Nithya Arunananda (Kamalini
Sathyanarayana)
Bangalore, Karnataka, India
manithya.arunananda@gmail.com

Ma Nithya Deekshananda (A.S Sandhya)
Bangalore, Karnataka, India
assandhya@yahoo.com

Ma Nithya Dharmajananda
(Cheryl Kharwansan Rumnong)
Shillong, Meghalaya, India
cheryl.k.rumnong@gmail.com

Sri Nithyananda Yukteshwar
Ondipudur, Coimbatore
srinithyabharata@yahoo.co.in

MALAYSIA

Ma Nithyananda Soundriya
Bandar Bangu Bangi, Selangor, Malaysia
huideli@gmail.com

MOROCCO

Ma Nithya Kalananda (Francoise Bidan
Barkat)
Agadir, Morocco
sarvagataa@orange.fr

NEW ZEALAND

Ma Ananda Kalaadevi (Marilyn Carbone)
Rutora, New Zealand
ma.ananda.kalaadevi@ihug.co.nz

SINGAPORE

Ma Nithyananda Arpana
nithyananda.arpana@gmail.com

Sri Nithya Arpanananda
nithya.arpananda@gmail.com

TURKEY

Ma Nithya Abhishekananda (Nayad Bal)
Caddebostan Kadikoy, Istanbul, Turkey
nayaddevi@hotmail.com

UNITED ARAB EMIRATES

Ma Nithyananda Atma Prema (Sandhya
Nambiar)
Dubai, United Arab Emirates
sandhya.nambiar@gmail.com

U.S.A

Ma Nithyananda Nischala
Phoenix, Arizona
nithyananda.nischala@gmail.com

Ma Nithyananda Bodhaana
Ohio, Columbus
nithyananda.bodhaana@gmail.com

Ma Nithyananda Premeshwari Mayi (Aarti Rao)
Michigan, Ann Arbour
nithyananda.premeshwari@gmail.com

Sri Ekan Nithya
Orlando, Florida
namaste1@lcy.com

Ma Nirgunavathi Ananda
Orlando, Florida
namaste1@lcy.com

Sri Nithyananda Muni
Los Angeles, California
nithyanandamuni@yahoo.com

Sri Nithya Yogadharman (Shailender Karuney)
Milpitas, California
nyogadharman@gmail.com